CW00549129

Toward a Phenomenology
of the Etheric World

Investigations into the Life
of Nature and Man

Editor:
Jochen Bockemühl

Anthroposophic Press, Inc.
Spring Valley, N. Y.

This volume is a translation of *Erscheinungsformen des Ätherischen*, Stuttgart, Verlag Freies Geistesleben 1977.

Library of Congress Cataloging in Publication Data

[Erscheinungsformen des Ätherischen. English]
  Toward a phenomenology of the etheric world.

  Translation of: Erscheinungsformen des Ätherischen.
  Bibliography: p.
  1. Anthroposophy—Addresses, essays, lectures.
I. Gardner, Malcolm, 1959-   . II. Davy, John.
BP595.E7713 1985   299'.935   84-21694
ISBN 0-88010-115-6

Cover: Graphic design by Rudolf Steiner made in 1923 for *Die ätherischen Bildekräfte in Kosmos, Erde und Mensch* by Guenther Wachsmuth.

Title lettering by Peter Stebbing.

Printed in the United States of America

Contents

Preface to the English Edition
Arthur G. Zajonc

What is the essence of life? Since at least the time of Aristotle this question has animated discussions in both practical and theoretical biology. The world of living organisms appears, in a completely self-evident way, radically different from the realm of inorganic matter. What is the fundamental basis and origin of this difference?

We may broaden the question. In any domain of scientific investigation regularities appear. Nature is seen as a "formed" reality, one which often demonstrates her active principles in strikingly beautiful phenomena. What processes or activities give rise to the forms of nature, animate or inanimate? Such questions strike at the very heart of our study of nature. They are questions that probe the very basis for reality, and as such have usually been spurned by the scientific community as being of only philosophic interest. Indeed, if one studies the history of science, it has often been philosophers such as Kant or Cassirer who have most thoroughly discussed the unique status of biological phenomena.

Yet one may inquire whether such a division is truly necessary or even fruitful. Can one uncover and practice a method of scientific investigation which, while strictly based on observation, searches for the essential character of life? According to Jochen Bockemühl, such a method would focus on those movements which lead to the formation and development of natural phenomena. That is, instead of attempting to discover molecular, mechanical or efficient causes, one can, by disciplined observation, learn to identify processes whose mutual interplay govern, for example, leaf metamorphosis. Certainly, what one actually sees are the momentary

v

stages in the plant's development. But within them we can learn to read the ideal processes or movements which, while unseen, clearly underlie leaf metamorphosis. Here one is approaching an essential aspect of the plant world. One is doing so not theoretically, nor through the kind of speculation characteristic of 19th century *Naturphilosophie*. Rather one is striving for what Goethe termed a "gentle empiricism" wherein the investigator, by becoming an active participant in nature, is able to experience and accurately conceive the formative movements of nature herself.

In bringing these seven essays together, Jochen Bockemühl has shown what he and others have accomplished in this direction. As director of the natural scientific studies at the School of Spiritual Science (the Goetheanum in Dornach, Switzerland), Dr. Bockemühl has worked intensively as a botanist and a student of Rudolf Steiner's anthroposophy. He brings before us his own efforts and those of like-minded colleagues in order that we may begin to understand and experience what Steiner called the *etheric*. Not to be confused with the hypothetical, material ether of 19th century physics, Steiner's etheric was for him the object of supersensible observation. Dr. Poppelbaum, in his essay included here, brings together in short compass something of what Rudolf Steiner wrote concerning this domain; and Steiner's many writings and lectures are readily available for further study. But what characterizes the remaining six essays most is their relative independence from the details of Rudolf Steiner's own discussions.

In the essays gathered here we see their reflections tend naturally in two directions which, perhaps surprisingly, are intimately connected: the genesis of form in nature, and the structured flow of human thinking. Working from indications by Rudolf Steiner, the common spiritual, etheric basis of these two realms becomes more and more evident. In thinking, as Emerson writes, nature repeats herself on a higher plane, so that we recognize in the processes of thought, activities not unlike those of assimilation, digestion, self-maintenance and creation. On the other hand, through attentive botanical studies, Bockemühl demonstrates that here too we confront "formative movements" which express themselves in the unfolding leaves. Thus out of a study of two realms, and from the gradual discernment of those formative movements that manifest in each, these scientists strive to learn of that spiritual reality whose presence we recognize in the worlds of thinking and of life. Here we find a valuable contribution to independent research based in what Steiner chose to call the "science of the spirit."

Introduction
Jochen Bockemühl

"It is not the task of science to propound questions; its task is rather to observe them carefully as they are posed by human nature and the culture of a particular time, and to answer them."

"It is by virtue of the constitution of the human soul that questions of knowledge arise when the outer world is perceived. In the soul's own impulse to question lies the power to penetrate the perceived world in such a way that it, together with the soul's activity, brings the reality of the perceived world to manifestation."

Rudolf Steiner[1]

For the attentive observer, there is ample evidence[2] that the method of understanding cultivated by natural science permits the objective world only a particular kind of question, and seeks answers only in a narrowly circumscribed direction. Such trenchant evidence alone, however, will not lead beyond these limitations until we become conscious of our own relationships to the world. Only by tracing the way questions originate in us, can we free ourselves from the conventionally determined way of answering.

In this volume we shall be concerned with experiences which direct us toward a realm which in Rudolf Steiner's spiritual science is called the *etheric world*. Although our intention is to extend natural science in this direction, it is not enough merely to systematize some new concepts (even those offered by spiritual science) and use them to classify the phenomena of the world in new ways. The essential problem is to develop a new relationship to our own thinking—through introspection—and thereby achieve a new and im-

ix

mediate experience of nature like the one Goethe was endowed with naturally. This publication contains examples of work where, out of a background of anthroposophy, the attempt is made to sensitize natural science to new forms of questions, and in pursuing these, to penetrate to deeper strata of reality.

Selection was not easy. The aim was to present *new* possibilities, as indicated above, for concerning ourselves scientifically with the level of the etheric.

Since the publication of Guenther Wachsmuth's books,[3] which were a first attempt to link Rudolf Steiner's spiritual science and the results of natural science, there have appeared in book form a whole series of other scientific efforts which are directly or indirectly related to this realm.[4] The work presented in this volume has not previously been published in book form.

The original intention was to assemble a number of existing papers into one volume, so as to make them available to a wider circle of readers. It became evident, however, that most of them needed to be rewritten. Only the paper by H. Poppelbaum was originally written for another purpose (it formed the lead article in the *Anthroposophisch-Medizinischen Jahrbuch*, vol. 3). It is included unaltered here, because in important ways it stimulated much of the more recent work, and because the *Jahrbuch* itself is no longer in print. (The references have been brought up to date.)

As we are here concerned with new territory, which can only be entered consciously with the help of practice, the content of these essays will remain inaccessible to anyone who is not ready to tread the inner path suggested here, at least for a short distance, and acquire some independent experience. For one who practices, new territory opens up with every step. The etheric world does not lie somewhere in the distance. It permeates us and the sense world that surrounds us. It is part of the world, only one which we are not usually conscious of.

The methodical rigor practiced in natural science, and the thought-experiences common to mathematics or geometry, are the only capacities that can ensure that we are not led astray with these exercises. With them, however, our viewpoint will change markedly. Thus, on the one hand, it will be noticed that so-called "facts" do not consist of pure sense percepts, they also contain the inner activity whereby we become aware of them. This activity corresponds to a mode of "illumination" by virtue of which the world becomes visible to us in a particular way. This unheeded process of illumination will merit special attention.

On the other hand, one will realize that the starting point for any activity of a mathematical nature is a content which at first is foreign to us. This content is taken up by our soul and brought into motion in such a way that the most disparate relations are seen to be interconnected. Thereby, the spiritual nature of the content is revealed. Seen in this way, the restriction of our "mathematizing" activity to mathematical content alone is no longer necessary. One discovers that this mathematizing activity can also apprehend the images derived from the sense world and bring to consciousness the spirituality which expresses itself through them. Herewith we have indicated the connection between the outer world and our inner activity; this can be pursued further along the path to higher faculties of cognition described in anthroposophy.[5]

Notes

1. See further Steiner, Rudolf. *A Theory of Knowledge Implicit in Goethe's World Conception* (1886). Spring Valley, N.Y.: Anthroposophic Press 1968. The motto stems from a passage (and its footnote) in the first chapter.

2. See for instance Heitler, Walter. *Man and Science* (1961). New York: Basic Books 1963.

3. Wachsmuth, Guenther. *The Etheric Formative Forces in Cosmos, Earth and Man* (1924). London: Rudolf Steiner Pub. Co. 1932.

— *Die ätherische Welt in Wissenschaft, Kunst und Religion.* Dornach: Philosophisch-Anthroposophischer Verlag 1927.

4. Adams, George. *Physical and Ethereal Spaces* (1933). London: Rudolf Steiner Press 1965.

— *Strahlende Weltgestaltung* (1934). 2nd ed. Dornach: Philosophisch-Anthroposophischer Verlag 1965.

— and Olive Whicher. *The Plant between Sun and Earth* (1952). 2nd ed. London: Rudolf Steiner Press 1980.

Bessenich, Frieda. *Zur Methode der empfindlichen Kristallisation.* Dornach: Philosophisch-Anthroposophischer Verlag 1960.

— *Beiträge zur Erforschung der Bildekrafte durch empfindliche Kristallisation.* Dornach: Naturwissenschaftlichen Sektion am Goetheanum 1951.

Fyfe, Agnes. *Moon and Plant. Capillary Dynamic Studies* (1967). 2nd ed. Arlesheim, Switz.: Society for Cancer Research 1975.

— *The Signature of the Planet Mercury in Plants* (reprint from "The British Homeopathic Journal," 1973-74). London.

Grohmann, Gerbert. *The Plant: A Guide to Understanding its Nature* vol. 1 (1948). London: Rudolf Steiner Press 1974; vol. 2, *Die Pflanze: Ein Weg zum Verständnis ihres Wesens* (1951). 3rd ed. Stuttgart: Verlag Freies Geistesleben 1981.

— *Die Pflanze als Lichtsinnesorgan der Erde* (essays 1948-1955). Stuttgart: Verlag Freies Geistesleben 1962.

Kolisko, Lilli. *Physiologischer und physikalischer Nachweis der Wirksamkeit kleinster Entitäten* (1923-1959). Stuttgart 1959.

Lehrs, Ernst. *Man or Matter.* (1950). 2nd ed. London: Harper and Bros. 1958.

Locher-Ernst, Louis. *Geometrische Metamorphose* (essays 1947-1951). Dornach: Philosophischer-Anthroposophischer Verlag 1970.

— *Raum und Gegenraum: Einführung in die neuere Geometrie* (1957). 2nd ed. Dornach: Philosophisch-Anthroposophischer Verlag 1970.

Marti, Ernst. *The Four Ethers* (1974). Roselle, Ill.: Schaumburg Pub. 1984.

Schatz, Paul. *Rhythmusforschung und Technik.* Stuttgart: Verlag Freies Geistesleben 1975.

Schwenk, Theodor. *Sensitive Chaos* (1962). New York: Schocken Books 1976.

— *Grundlagen der Potenzforschung* (1954). 3rd ed. Stuttgart: Verlag Freies Geistesleben 1974.

— *Bewegungsformen des Wassers. Nachweis feinster Qualitätsunterschiede mit der Tropfenbild-Methode.* Stuttgart 1967.

5. Steiner R., and Ita Wegman. *Fundamentals of Therapy* (1925). 4th ed. London: Rudolf Steiner Press 1983. Chapter 1.

Steiner, R. *The Boundaries of Natural Science* (1920). Spring Valley, N.Y.: Anthroposophic Press 1983. See especially the lectures of October 2 and 3, 1920.

Elements and Ethers:
Modes of Observing the World
Jochen Bockemühl

Introduction

The elements and the ethers can be characterized, not only as components of the world, but also as "an organism of mutually complementary ways of looking at the world," as an organism into which one can grow, therein to experience the mysteries of the world. We will attempt to illustrate the possibilities that arise in this way with the example of two closely related but very different plants. The fundamental aspects of such an approach can be shown particularly well with plants, but this approach can also enliven our powers of understanding in other realms, for instance the realm of light, which the succeeding contribution explores (p. 69ff.).

Our Relation to the World in Cognition—
Classification and the Modes of Observation

Our relation to nature is largely determined by the set of mental pictures with which we live, and by the often still automatic way in which we manage our consciousness.

We normally find ourselves surrounded by a world of objects which seem capable of existing independently of our consciousness of them. We believe we see objects outside ourselves, and do not notice that in order for them to appear as such, we must picture them to ourselves in a particular way. We mostly overlook the fact that the reality of these objects derives from the joining of two experiences which are gained in quite different ways: the percept coming from without, and the concept brought forth from within.[1]

1

While our awareness is completely turned away from ourselves and directed to the external object, something occurs within ourselves that fundamentally affects the character of what we see.

Observing a tree, we are often content to look at it from one side only. Without realizing it, we picture the tree as a whole. We add to what the percept provides, as though we had seen the object completely. When, in contrast, we walk around the tree and observe it from all sides, our impressions are much more comprehensive. If we then look again at the tree from the first point of view, the impressions from the other points of view flow together in our mind to make a meaningful picture.

That which allows us to picture the tree as a whole—the inner supplement—always comes out of ourselves. The two cases described above differ only in *how* the inner supplement arises. In the first case, what we add does not necessarily correspond to the actual tree. Without reflection, it forms itself out of a variety of experiences made on other occasions. In the walk around the tree, however, we acquire by means of the object itself a picture of the tree which is in accordance with its true and full appearance, which is, in other words, in accordance with reality.

A way of knowing that seeks reality solely in laws, proceeds mainly as in the first example above. The full content of the different percepts is passed over, because they are only of interest insofar as they conform to or depart from these laws. The more comprehensive the knowledge of such laws and the judgments based on them, the less need there is to concern oneself with the direct percepts. A quick glance is enough to establish and classify what is seen ("Aha! A maple . . .").

It is easy to see that in this way one begins to withdraw from the world, convinced that one now knows its nature because one has learned to manipulate the objects in it. But the interest in the world dwindles thereby. It will revive again only when something fundamental changes in the human being in his relationship to his own faculties of cognition. For this to occur, it is necessary to make conscious and to control one's own activity during cognition.

To begin with, we can notice that the laws which we experience as finished and external, are actually found *within us* as concepts. We think these in a particular form, and then seek their confirmation in the sense world. In daily life we reckon on finding these thoughts present in the world. In scientific experimentation we normally proceed in a similar manner: the arrangement of the experiment embodies a thought, which encompasses only a particular kind of outer object or process. The result of the experiment is taken as circumstantial evidence for the correctness of the particular train of thought which preceded the experiment. All the while, our attention is directed entirely toward the object of the experiment.[2]

Only when we bring this relationship to consciousness do we become aware that our thinking is an inner activity which can connect us with the world in a different manner from our sense percepts. The sense world then appears as the expression of a world which we have access to only through our thinking, a thought world which permeates the sense world.[3] Now we can observe the *kind* of activity within which a law or a concept lives, and make use of this to consider the world more consciously. Thus, the concept which was previously bound to the "object," is now freed in our consciousness and becomes merely one way of looking at the world. Each concept contains a different activity, a different way of directing ourselves to the world.[4] I notice, for example, an opposite branching pattern in the limbs of a tree. Thereby I become aware that I am regarding the tree from the aspect of branching patterns. This aspect covers all possible types of branching, and can be subdivided into narrower aspects like "opposite" or "alternate."

The awareness of this relationship leads me beyond the classification of the branching habit of this tree. I learn to direct my attention to the question: in what way is the special branching habit of *this* tree an expression of its nature?[5]

Thus, what I see in the world is dependent upon the concepts which guide my seeing. To begin with, it does not matter whether these are prompted from without or within, whether they are summoned consciously or unconsciously. Each concept formed in this way can be experienced as a light that illuminates the world. The sense world then presents the special form in which reality appears in the light of this concept.

When the concept is experienced as a *classification discovered in the world*, its character is to exclude, and as it embraces an ever wider variety of phenomena, it becomes ever emptier. With such concepts, we separate ourselves from the world. Experienced as a *specific form of illumination*, on the other hand, the concept becomes richer and fuller, the more that single phenomena can be seen as related in its light. In this way we "grow together" with the world that surrounds us.

Attentive observation of the world can awaken our inner capacity to illuminate it. Awareness of this capacity leads us to experience the interrelationships of the world. The illuminating power of thought becomes for us a picture of a unifying activity coming from the periphery of the world, an activity which would resolve all the separate entities of the sense world into the unity of the cosmos, an activity with which we feel ourselves to be inwardly related. This is the picture that Rudolf Steiner repeatedly used to describe the activity of the "cosmos," the "etheric," or the "world ether."[6] In itself—undifferentiated—the etheric cannot be grasped by us. Yet, when we look at the world, our inner capacity of illumination is always differentiated in some way. Thus the etheric cosmos appears differentiated to us. The etheric acquires its form and completion from a super-ordinated realm, the astral.[7] Each concept, as the source of a specific illumination, highlights a particular aspect of the world and comes from a particular direction of the universe.

This differentiated world of the etheric, stands in contrast to the experience of foreignness that comes to us through the senses and leads us to see separated objects. The direct relations we discover between these "foreign" objects leads us to say: "They have an effect on each other." We conceive these effects as emanating from the centers of these objects, from points. Such effects are described by Rudolf Steiner as physical, terrestrial, or earthly, and are contrasted with those of the ether or cosmos.[8] The "foreign," "dark" world of objects in the sense world could not be grasped cognitively were they not also clothed in something thought-like. We see substances, crystals, plants, animals, human beings. Everything that we experience through the senses as formed, is this thought-quality in an individualized condition.

In this manner we find the world divided into the four kingdoms of nature. In a similar fashion we can also find a division of the world which does not lead us to single entities such as plants and animals, but which expresses itself instead in *how* the "foreign" objects of the sense world relate to their surroundings. This leads us to the elements: earth, water, air and warmth.[9] This division of the sense world into different "layers," experienced at first purely outwardly, can, when we look inwardly, make us aware of the different layers of our thinking. As with the kingdoms of nature, we meet the elements outside, embodied as it were, and yet we find their reality within us. More will be said of this as we proceed.

In contrast, we can notice that although at first all the phenomena of the surrounding world appear isolated, these phenomena nevertheless stand in direct connection with each other. Our combinatory thinking bears the shadows of these connections, and from these we can proceed to find in our surroundings the "contextual" reality in which we are included. Layers also emerge here, according to whether we attend to *the context of all the phenomena revealed to the senses at one moment*, or whether we attend to *the sequence of such contextual phenomena* (for example through the course of the year), or whether we consider the *context of a life cycle*. These layers we can call layers of the etheric, or "ethers."

The elements and the ethers thus correspond to layers of distinct relationships in the phenomenal world, and these layers can be discovered only by means of several distinct modes of observation.

Rudolf Steiner points to the significance of Aristotle's categories in connection with a renewed "reading in the book of nature."[10] In relation to the present discussion, these categories, such as quality, quantity, etc., may be understood as concepts which, taken as *observational modes* [*Betrachtungsweisen*], can open up the different realms of reality for us. Applied to the same natural phenomena, they open our eyes to the diverse, self-contained areas of reality, whose relations with each other are revealed in pure thinking.

With the concept of the elements and ethers as modes of observation, we should now like to approach some specific workings of the world. As was described earlier with the example of the tree, the aim with each observational mode will be to attain a complete picture of what is at first experienced as an isolated observation. We do this through inner contemplation of our experiences, and therewith set foot on the path to an Imaginative perception of the world.[11]

The Elements and the Ethers as Ways in which the World
Reveals Itself to the Corresponding Modes of Observation.

A plant in a garden, on a sunny morning in early summer, appears to us immediately as a unity. The content of this first impression cannot be expressed. It appears like a question, offering possibilities of many answers.

If one attempts to become conscious of the plant, one may say things like: "The plant is beautiful!" It has large red flowers with conspicuous yellow-orange pollen." "The flowers do not extend far beyond the luxuriant bushy foliage." With each such utterance, one brings the immediate observation into relation with other experiences. Usually this is done unconsciously. If we become aware, however, of how we ourselves make the connections between what we are observing and what we are remembering, we then become conscious of the possibility of making mistakes. Yet we also find in us the force which gives us the confidence to speak of facts in our observation, and which enables us to define the limits of each statement. We discover this force in our striving for truth.[12]

Seeing how we can make mistakes, we try to be particularly wakeful in this process of making judgments. Thus we observe that not all the leaves on our bush come from one stem, as it first appeared. There are several shoots with leaves, and some of the leaves grow directly out of the soil.

A great many details come into our consciousness: the large juicy leaves, with wavy edges, some with stems, the rounded buds, etc. We can connect the details with one another, arrange them in order, and create a conceptual image of the plant. A botanical identification manual, with its detailed dichotomous key, can be a big help in distinguishing one species from another. Because the large undoubled flowers arise singly at the end of a shoot, and because the leaves are pinnately compound, we can identify the plant as the wild form of the Peony (*Paeonia officinalis*). The process

is now complete, for we know what plant we saw. The Peony
has been identified (see Illustration 1).

But let us remember the first impression. Was it not in
many respects richer than the clear and detailed picture we
now have? My process of understanding has reached a certain conclusion, but something remains unsatisfactory. I
have to admit that taking the identification of the plant as
my objective was in fact quite arbitrary. Do I really know
what I have named? One could go much further with the
description of this mode of observation. Within each detail,
many more details would have revealed themselves. What
the eye could not see would be revealed by the microscope,
by chemical analysis, etc. But thereby, that which at first
enabled me to see all the characters as a unity, that which
gave me the courage to say the name "Peony," remains hidden, although it helps me now to bring the details together
into one "system."

This is the situation of science at present: it provides a
growing awareness of the details, but what is observed
becomes schematic. In the process one becomes blind to the
unity—in this case the concept of the Peony—which is presupposed in every act of predication. The unity is not the
fancied system, but rather the concept that conceals itself
within it.

Earth, the Solid Element

We seem to have reached a limit to knowing. But that
very feeling of dissatisfaction aroused by the abstract
description of the plant can make us aware that we did in
fact experience more of the plant than we could make conscious through studying it as an object in the way described.

Should we not attend to the form of those questions that
lead beyond what we already know, and adjust our mode of
observing the plant accordingly?

We can note, for example, the following: the description of the Peony could also include, with equal validity, details such as "biennial," or "flowers end of May to early June." These are references to the way the plant is related to time. But in the conceptual statement, all these qualities, which are actually processes and transformations, lose their characteristic outer and inner movement. They become *established* [*festgestellt*—literally, made solid]. In the described manner, the Peony is grasped only insofar as it is a solid object.

The more inward aspects of phenomena—be they stones or organisms—must remain hidden from us as long as we observe from outside. The attitude of the detached observer consists precisely in bringing all that is inward, into the form of externality—for example, by dissecting the plant in order to investigate its cell structure and fluids. The conceptions gained from such external observation cannot be mentally transferred back inside without violating our sense of truthfulness.

We experience the impenetrability of the perceived world for our object-consciousness. We have the impression that the real essence of what we are observing lies behind what we perceive, and still our method of observation reveals to us only more, similarly external perceptions. It slowly becomes clear to us that we come to *firm* conclusions, that we are always *limited to the surface* of things and see them as *separate*, exactly because the qualities of *solidity, impenetrability* and *separateness* are rooted in our cognitional attitude itself. This attitude can be characterized, following Maier,[13] as having the quality of the earth element.

There are phenomena, for example stones, but especially objects made by human beings, which can rightly be grasped in many respects with the "solid" mode of observation, and which we therefore describe as solid objects. What we call "solid," or "earth element," thus shows itself to be the outer picture of a particular quality of experience we have in our thinking when we as detached observers, try progressively to grasp the sense world with individual mental pictures.

Water, the Fluid Element

The solid element can only be described in the preceding manner if one has already become aware of experiences which make other modes of observation seem possible. But once one has become aware of such possibilities, our daily experience offers ample starting points for a change in our cognitional attitude.

To begin with, I would like to indicate two such starting points. The first is found in the sense world, the world of appearances. I do not really see the Peony only as a solid object. Even in the spatial picture of the plant I see a transformation. This impression can be strengthened by collecting all the leaves of one plant and laying them side by side (see Figure 1). Although I thereby cut the leaves off from their outer connection with the living plant, and emphasize the distinctness of the single forms, now that they are in one plane, I become aware of a sequential change in the forms— a "movement" which is not present for the senses as movement in the normal sense.

Transformations similar to those of form can also be seen in coloration. We may follow the leaves of Wild Lettuce— delicate light green at the top, dark juicy green in the middle leaves, becoming yellow lower down, turning reddish brown near the ground. Such perceptions link themselves with memories of growing, changing, and dying plants. The richer such experience, the surer grasp we shall have of the new perceptions we have gained in connection with the transformations we are following.

It is evident that here we are no longer only concerned with sense percepts. Our attention is directed to processes

Second year   *Third year*

Figure 1 (pp. 11–15). Complete leaf sequence of a Peony (*Paeonia officinalis*) over six years after sowing.

which play themselves out between sense perception and inner soul experience. It is also evident that we seldom become conscious of this. The separate appearances swim into our awareness and link themselves together as in a dream. Before we are aware of what is happening, the process is held in our consciousness as a frozen picture of a completed process. Evidently we make use here of a capacity in which the inner soul experience, rather than opposing the percept, actively connects itself with it. What had frozen comes into movement, only to rigidify again. But during the period of movement, inwardness and outwardness lose their boundaries.

Here we become aware of a mode of observation which we employ continually, but most often in a dreamlike way. It leads us not only to the surfaces of things, it unites us with their processes.

The reality of the *solid* element is always experienced wherever a percept as a finished product is nailed down by a concept. The characteristic of the *fluid* element is that it molds itself to its surroundings or tries to form an even, all-embracing surface. The forms in flowing water are pictures which are unified in and through the movement.[14] What appears as a mobile picture is an expression both of its own nature and of its surroundings.

11

Peony. Leaf sequence in fourth year.

The plant too can be grasped as a "flowing form" when our imaginative activity molds itself to one form and then dissolves this again as it flows on toward the next form. Our own activity can thus merge with what we observe. Thereby, an ideal movement arises, which is a kind of counter-picture to the individual forms. This mobile spiritual connection, the living mental picture, is as real as the picture derived from the separate forms of the sense world. Using an expression of Splechtner's, we will call this living mental picture a "formative movement" [*Bildebewegung*].[15]

It is mentioned only in passing that a single form also is grasped with the help of a corresponding ideal movement.

12

Peony. Leaf sequence in fifth year.

Here it need only be said that in the latter case the *finished* form is emphasized, whereas with the formative movement it is the movement itself that is sought.[16] Both perception and comprehension must achieve a higher level of awareness if we would learn to move freely as knowers in the reality of the watery element. Although we actually live in this element with our imaginative activity, this activity is usually accompanied only by dimly conscious feelings; we normally *wake up* only when we bump into something, i.e. only in the finished mental picture. It can now be easily seen, that it is in principle impossible to *live* in the solid element, i.e. also not with our consciousness. But in being brought to a halt, in

Peony. Leaf sequence in sixth year, with first flower.

falling out of the living, there waking consciousness arises. Our *own* life and being extend as far as this consciousness.

The Fluid Mode of Observation
Applied to Plant Development

We may now consider more fully the "fluid" mode of observation with the help of two examples, the Peony and

the Stinking Hellebore (*Helleborus foetidus*). Let us first take a flowering shoot of the Peony (Illus. 1). Below, the shoot and the petioles are as green as the leaves. Further up, the green contracts toward the main stem. Above this the flower unfolds with new forms and colors. It is a new appearance, but it comes from the same stem. To grasp this transformation more clearly we can distinguish the successive parts by

15

cutting them off (Fig. 1). We can then see the threefold expansion and contraction of foliage, flower and fruit, which Goethe described. A striking characteristic of the Peony is the large jump from the lowest, very simple scale-like leaf, to the first true foliage leaf. This stands in strong contrast to the gradual transition of the contraction into the calyx-like leaves (see especially Fig. 1, sixth year). (This sequence is reversed in the Dandelion, for example, which develops its leaves one after another in a rosette close to the ground, and then as it were, "jumps" to the flower without any intermediate contracted forms.) The leaf form itself can also be grasped as a movement. Its gesture is directed mainly outward, with a spreading surface, articulated and somewhat compact, but tapered at the same time.

In the sequence of leaf forms, the contracting phase is expressed in the shortening of the stem, in the reduction in the size of the whole leaf, and in the narrowness and pointedness of the leaflets. It is relatively easy to picture the transformation to the flower in the Peony. As the leaf dwindles, its base begins to widen and become colored. We can then follow a second contraction in two directions: to the stamens which bear dry pollen that scatters outwards, and to the carpels which bear the moist, delicate ovules close to the stem.[17] After the union of these two, the final expansion comes with the swelling of the fruit and the formation of seeds within.

★

When we follow these forms, it is easy to overlook the fact that in simply picturing the changes, we do not come fully to grips with the particular characteristics of the stages of leaf, flower and fruit formation. Here Wigand's[18] concepts can help: sequential metamorphosis of the leaves, adjacent metamorphosis in the parts of the flower, and interpenetrant metamorphosis between fruit and seed. These make clear the differences in the levels of development. But to see the connection between the way a particular species of plant expresses itself in leaf, flower and fruit, one must penetrate further. The continuity of the species through the metamorphosis of appearances cannot be grasped with mobile picturing alone. What is needed can only be indicated at this stage: it will depend on the extent to which the observer can succeed in finding, despite the different levels of manifestation, a consistent "gesture." In other words, one must rediscover in the appearance of the flower what one experienced earlier as the particular transformational quality of the leaf. The transition to fruit and seed formation is still more difficult to find. The outer appearance offers hardly a clue. And yet the whole plant's developmental potential is contained in the seed. Here we come to the limit of the "fluid" mode of observation and touch on further modes which we will consider later. But first we must look more closely at the Peony's course of development.

The shoot we have been studying grew very rapidly out of the earth, its young leaves in the forefront, and spread itself out. Gradually the spherical flower buds swelled until they burst open. The red blossoms shone for a while. When the large petals wilted, the foliage and sepals remained green, tinged with red (they only wilt as the seeds ripen). To follow the development of such a shoot, one must go back many years, and also take into account what goes on beneath the surface of the soil (Illus. 2).

In the example shown here we can follow how a four-lobed leaf appeared one and a half years after sowing (the cotyledons remained in the soil). This leaf persisted into the summer. Meanwhile, below the soil a thickened root and a bud formed. In the third year a second foliage leaf appeared, more fully differentiated, which again lasted into

Figure 2 (pp. 18-33). Complete leaf sequence of a Stinking Hellebore (*Helleborus foetidus*) from germination to flower over five years.

the summer. At the same time, the root thickened further and a new subterranean bud formed. In the fourth year, three leaves appeared on a slender shoot without a flower. Thereafter two subterranean buds were formed and in the fifth year we saw two sturdy and more heavily-leaved shoots emerge, though with tiny stunted flower buds. Only in the sixth year, did two strong flowering shoots form, which later bore fine black shiny seeds (see also Illus. 3 and 4).

Slowly, over several years, the plant has built up its strength, repeatedly rising up, becoming more leafy, and repeatedly concentrating its forces into the earth. Whatever appeared above the ground each year, including the flowers, already lay prepared in miniature in the subterranean buds of the previous year. The manner in which the plant grew over the years is mirrored in the increasingly large and well-differentiated leaves. The first leaves of each new shoot are more rounded to begin with; only in later years do they attain the pointed lobes, the typical form. As though from an increasing concentration of strength, the new shoot always bears the largest leaf. The progressive contraction of the successive leaves, which eventually forms the transition to

18

Hellebore. Leaf sequence in first and second year (pp. 18–20).

the flower and fruit, is accompanied by a thickening of the root wherein the forces for the following year are concentrated. In the root system dissected out of the six-year-old plant (see Illus. 2), the finger-thick root swellings are very apparent. They are reddish brown, rather watery and have a sharp taste, almost like horseradish.

★

The characteristic features of the Peony's course of development become clearer when contrasted with a close relative, the Stinking Hellebore (*Helleborus foeditus*, Illus. 9). This plant also develops over several years, but in a more uniform way (see Illus. 7). It grows stronger each year, but bears green leaves continuously (they die back only after new ones have formed). It does not withdraw each year into the earth and does not form such thick swollen roots. The numerous root fibers are brownish, watery and glassy. The shoot grows further each year. Its older portions may lie on the ground and put out new roots. When after a number of years the plant flowers, the whole inflorescence is light green. The flowers and the upper leaves are almost the same

19

color. Only the outer margins of the petals acquire a dark reddish tinge.

The uniformity of development of this plant is mirrored in the leaf forms (Fig. 2). They are dark green and leathery, with long, finely serrated pointed blades; in contrast to the Peony, they show only limited changes of form. Leaves with large broad surfaces are followed by smaller, tufted forms. The latter usher in the transition to the flower. Before the flower emerges, the leaf base, which is already light green, broadens. Before the petals come, several dark green leaves with longer tufts are formed again; then finally, the leaf becomes simpler and contracts. Thus, before the flower, while seemingly in the phase of contraction, the leaf once more exhibits an expansion and a contraction.

At this level, we have been attending to the formative movements of both plants, and we see how their characteristic forms come to expression in quite distinct ways. A next step will be to attempt to indicate how these formative movements lead us to a "physiognomic element."

Hellebore. Leaf sequence in third year (pp. 21–25).

Concerning the "Expression" of the Plant

With the mode of observation corresponding to the watery element, it becomes possible to go beyond the single elements of form and reach a realm not directly accessible to sense perception; here the sequence of forms appears as formative movement, and the formative forces can be experienced. If something is observed as an *object*, it is always seen from the outside, it is seen separately and seemingly from all sides at once. There, one's own standpoint is unimportant. The object exists without me. If, however, one begins to become aware of the formative forces in the way described, one's own inner activity (intentionality) and one's own position within the whole become significant. Because we are no longer regarding things as objects, it is clear that concepts such as expansion and contraction relate to experiences in thinking. It then becomes significant whether I follow a leaf sequence as though I were myself living within the changing leaf, or whether I identify myself with the surroundings out of which the leaf forms and reforms itself.

21

Whether I experience a force as working "from within" or "from without," depends on the place from which I am looking, or the direction in which I move with my picturing. The "space" which is implied here should not be confused with merely external space. What is meant is described pictorially, but it is distinguished by the dynamic experience it entails.

If we follow the developmental stages of a plant, we become aware of its specific kinds of transformation (compare the description in the previous section). One learns, so to speak, to grow with the plant, to change with it, to follow inwardly all the transformations in the region of the foliage leaves. One sees how from below the bulk of the vegetation emerges and is pushed upwards and outwards, and how the root system infiltrates itself into the firm surroundings of the earth.

Higher up the plant one can follow the refining of the parts, the contraction of the leaves into pointed forms, and anticipate the transition to flowering. One can see how flowering and fruiting are a continuing metamorphosis at successively higher stages. With the help of the plant's developing life, one learns to make one's own experience inwardly active and mobile.

Nevertheless, also this mode of observation reaches a limit. We can follow all the changes of a plant, and learn

something of its formative forces, but what eludes us is the direct experience that a Peony awakens in our soul, and its characteristic gesture that we see in its appearance. This characteristic gesture we will call the *expression* [*Bildausdruck*]. This expression is most distinct when the plant flowers. This flowering, in which growth is checked and the plant becomes the outer image of a being, cannot be fully grasped out of the flowing quality of the watery element.

*

We have seen how an individual plant may be externally described as an object. As a second step, its growth and formation can be grasped with mobile, pictorial thinking, in which we unite ourselves with the interconnected processes whereby the plant grows and develops. But the meaning of the plant, its "physiognomic expression," only becomes apparent when we attend to the *being* that is expressing itself— rather as the wrinkles on a human face have meaning only in relation to the whole countenance.

The memory of the first undefined yet total impression made on us by the Peony, can help us find a further mode of observation beyond that which we have termed the watery mode. We need a mode which can help us grasp the expression both in the flower and in the whole plant.

A new inner activity is needed now. Fundamentally, we

need only to practice what the plant itself shows us in its metamorphosis: after the leaves have reached their greatest expansion they become finer, lie closer to the stem, hold back their tendency to spread out, and then as leaf, almost disappear into a spine that together with the shoot reaches toward the light. There, at the tip of the shoot, where the growing forces are held back, the complete flower appears, as though from another world—something entirely new. Just as in the single leaf the first green tip announces the sprouting plant (see the essay on formative movements, p. 131ff.), so the flower bud, with its closely appressed leaflets around the shoot-tip, anticipates—when half open—the gesture of the flower, and—when still closed—the gesture of the fruit. At flowering, the previously developed foliage is held back, and something higher appears in the open blossom. The plant blossoms out to a higher being. As though from above, this entity descends into what has been prepared from below, and becomes a "picture." (Refer once again to Illus. 1 and 9).

If we are to follow this gesture, this means first of all, that we must concentrate upon, and inwardly produce "that which has yet to appear." Our own activity has to be held back, and the forces thus gained must be allowed, as it were, to stream outwards as attentiveness, making themselves available for the appearance of something higher.

24

This gesture of self-dissipation, of offering the image the opportunity to appear and to speak, we find in the element of air.

Air, the Element of Acquiescence

We often regard the airy element as though it were a kind of refined fluid. With appropriate means, we can make visible certain air movements which resemble those of water. In this way, air is shown to be related to water, just as a still, unmoving body of water can be related to the element of earth.

But such pictures obscure the differences, and tend to make us overlook the other, much more significant features of the air element. Although to some degree we can experience it directly as an external presence, we are mainly aware of it indirectly. As an object, the air eludes us almost completely. It makes way for the visible appearances of things. The objects of our environment are perceived through it, as are also the blue of the sky and the colors of the atmosphere. Wherever something has condensed, as a solid body, as a fluid, as a fine haze, the appearances are mediated to our senses through the selfless presence of the air.

Terrestrial objects look clearer and more external, the purer the surrounding air, i.e. the less the air appears to

Hellebore. Leaf sequence in fourth year (pp. 26–32).

contain anything itself. With different degrees of turbidity—
that is to say, in connection with the fluid element—the
atmosphere itself becomes a play of color, it becomes lit up
and awakens in us an experience which is not based on the
"externalness" of the phenomena.[19] A similar process occurs with the sounds that the air mediates.

On the other hand, the more outward activity of the air—
its capacity for movement, compression, rarefaction, and
desiccation—is not directly visible but becomes apparent in
the movements of trees and their leaves, in the flight and
sound of birds, and in the drying out of the soil. It is characteristic of air to expand in all directions, offering its own
being and activity in order that the being and activity of
another can appear.

Insofar as we move inwardly in accordance with this image of the air, we reach the cognitional attitude corresponding to the air element. An inner readiness is thus created for
that which manifests in the world to reveal itself in us, as an
image which discloses a being.

With this cognitional attitude an archetypal image is revealed to us when we see how the Rose struggles up out of
the thorny wood of the stem, how it creates sharply toothed

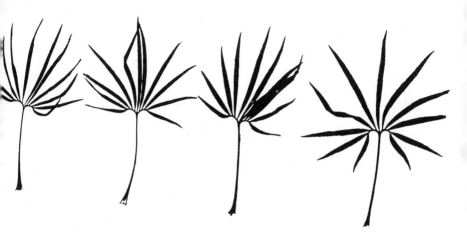

leaf forms, and how—seemingly from below, out of inward purity—it blossoms forth, shining red and delicately scented.[20]

The Peony makes a living picture for us through the rhythmic and rapid upward growth and the strong contraction of the thickened root; through, on the one hand, the lush, bright red blossom—its scent at once flowery and yet somewhat vegetative and foul—and, on the other hand, the long root-swellings with their sharp horseradish-like smell and taste. It resembles the Rose (indeed there are related species with woody stems which grow into large bushes). Yet in comparison to the Rose, it is softer, juicier, less regular. It is as though the Peony's forms grew out of the watery element and then condensed and thickened.

In comparison, the development of the Stinking Hellebore is more moderate, more self-contained. The flower and fruit formation, in color as well as smell, do not emerge so emphatically out of the vegetative realm.

The images indicated here only really become expressive when considered in the context of the whole environment, as we shall do later. At present we are merely concerned with the level where imaginal manifestation becomes possible.

27

Warmth, the Element of Inner Activity and Impulse

In order to understand the elements of earth and water we can orient ourselves directly by their external appearance. A stone's solid form and impenetrability are characteristics which bring us and our experience to a limit: we meet up with something foreign.

We become aware of ourselves in contrast to the things around us, and may thus experience ourselves as a captive of our own horizon. We resemble the solid element when we try to hold fast to something that we have or want to possess, or when we try to define our concepts exactly.

The fluctuation of water between adapting to its surroundings and making its own all-embracing form, between molding itself around an object and dissolving the same, is a picture that leads us to a quite different experience. We move in the fluid element when we try to follow the contours of the entities which surround us, to flow around them, harmonize and seek connections between them. Thereby, everything comes into movement, loses its defined forms, and is comprehended in a state of constant change.

In experiencing the movement from one sense impression to the next, we ourselves hold the connection. The transforming activity of both the artist and the creative thinker lives in this element.

The elements of air and warmth offer much less in the way of an outer appearance than do earth and water. Air, as we have seen, is barely perceptible. It surrounds us and penetrates into us. We never stand apart from it. We experience it as materiality in condensation and rarefaction; it is something that is always endeavoring to expand into the world, to disperse itself, i.e. to dissipate its own substance and make room for the manifestations of sound and light. In the air, the images of the ethers themselves can appear. We resemble the air insofar as we open ourselves to sense impressions, seemingly sucking them in as we spread them out before us; we offer our own activity to their revelations and grasp what we thus receive. We also live in the airy element when we receive the light of ideas and compress them into our consciousness.

Of all the elements, warmth is the least independent of

us. We can see and experience it only in the image of fire. And even here, the materiality of this image is provided by the other elements. We experience warmth directly—either within us or as the condition of our environment relative to us. It is the element which penetrates and energizes everything, and which also can destroy everything from within. Without the element of warmth no inner or outer activity occurs, nothing happens. We live in the element of warmth when we gather ourselves to do something, or get warm doing it, and also in those moments when our own thought activity arises in and merges with another being.

Warmth can be perceived as something external. Yet we can distinguish our own awareness of this perception even less than with the other elements. We are intimately united with it. Warmth is an immediate presence, full of content but undifferentiated. Form and content can barely be separated. The transition from outer to inner is smooth and continuous.

We are here at the limit of what can be called a mode of observation. The warmth enters us—our inner activity itself becomes an organ. We do not experience the outer expression of a being, we become aware of its inner impulse. At

30

those moments of inner identity, all outer manifestations disappear. They are "burned up."

When we approach the plant in this way, we grasp how at the stage of seed formation the plant is inwardly concentrated, its outer expression in root, leaf and flower, rapidly dying away. In the spring, the new plant arises out of this center of possibilities.

Concerning the Peripheral Influences

By considering the plant in light of the elements, we gradually understand it more deeply. At first we understand it as an earthly object, with a defined form and an independent existence and activity. But this is only one aspect of its being. The plant also lives in the periphery. It grows into a relationship with that out of which it arises. As it develops, it increasingly becomes a picture of its surroundings. Usually we imagine the environment of the plant (and also of ourselves), as being made up of a number of "factors"—warmth, light, humidity, soil conditions, etc. But we can also experience our environment as a unity. We may indeed take in a variety of impressions through different senses, but we

make these into a unity. We can even recognize that this unity is the more primary aspect, which only becomes differentiated as it passes through the gates of the senses.

The fragmentation of the environment into a number of separate influences has arisen through the mode of thinking cultivated by physics. It fits in a world regarded as being made up of numerous separate effects, and it allows us to become aware of these. But we remain dissatisfied, because the original connection with the whole is thereby lost. How can we approach this unity once more? A first step lies in realizing that we bear something of this unity within our thinking.

In what follows, four distinct aspects of thinking will be described. They again reveal new layers of experience in the sense world. We become aware that qualities related to thinking are working at different levels in the world we perceive around us.

The Conscious Experience of the Context
of the World—The Activity of Thinking

There are close links between the observational modes which lead to the elements, and the observational modes which connect us with the activities of the periphery.

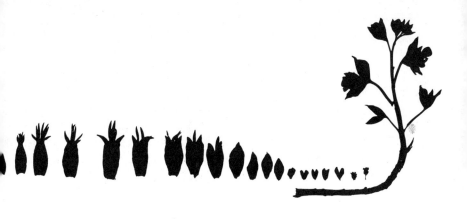

Hellebore. Leaf sequence in fifth year. Flowering shoot in February.

Through the solid element, we experience the world as permanent, but also capable of endless subdivision. Each part can be separately considered on its own. The less content possessed by each such part, the more abstract and external the relationships between them, which we describe as laws. This is easily shown in the development of modern science. We would completely lose ourselves in the details, and would be unable to think of laws at all, did we not trust (if only unconsciously) in a real relationship which, as a name, a concept, or a meaning, underlies all the details. We have shown this with the plant. It is striking that we can talk about the "Peony" at all, since strict scientific procedure only allows us to examine its individual characteristics one after the other. At the back of our minds there is evidently some kind of prior knowledge or judgment, which holds the connections. With our activity of thinking we feel ourselves directly connected to an entity which lives and works in the world. Observing that our desire for knowledge finds only temporary satisfaction in the establishment and classification of a myriad of details, we realize that this striving for knowledge is actually directed toward finding a "*context of meaning*" in the outer world. We bear the shadow of this

33

context of meaning within us as a concept. It requires, however, a gradual transformation of our powers of knowing in order to truly meet the reality that casts the shadow.

We are often unaware of the confidence we have in the context of meaning because we are distracted by the world of details and the laws through which the details are brought into external connection. The context of meaning is the force by which we know to what degree one phenomenon belongs to another. When we see a leaf we have never seen before, it allows us to say with certainty whether an indentation in the leaf margin belongs to the leaf, or is due to some external interference. Indeed, one can speak of a leaf having been "eaten into" only if one somehow pictures *the intact form* of a plant that one is *not* presently observing.

★

Through the fluid element, we experience how the world constantly transforms itself. If we abandon ourselves totally to this flowing and streaming activity, we might think that anything could change into any other thing. And yet we find order. The transformation of one form into another is not arbitrary. When we follow the development of a plant, or the course of a river, we experience the connection, the coherence, through all the transformations.

We would be completely at sea among the succession of our sense percepts, were we not confident that some one thing runs through them all and gives direction to the changes. In our thinking activity we feel ourselves intimately bound up with something that is active in the interconnections of the world. We unconsciously assume that through the different appearances of the plant or the river there runs a "*context of transformation*," which is accessible to thinking. We do not know the entity that is transforming itself, and yet we can deal with it. This entity reveals itself here as the new reality of *time*.

In an observational mode which attends to the context of transformation, we feel ourselves connected, not with the eaten part of the leaf in the example above, but with the wholeness of the plant's formative activity. In following the rhythm of the contour of a leaf, we are disturbed by the eaten section because it interrupts the coherent transformational context. On the other hand, it is possible to experience a regularity in the eaten section when the rhythmic feeding activity of a caterpillar is recognized there.

When following transformations, we are usually so identified with their coherent context that it is no longer noticed, or else in retrospect we relate the coherence to an abstract, externally imposed pattern (as, for example, when we confuse a rhythmic repetition of similar organs with a common "Bauplan" or "blueprint").

When we observe that, where there are processes of movement and transformation, rhythm arises, this points us to two things: a progressive aspect and a constant aspect, which work together. Our experience of change (progression) is closely linked with our experience of similarity (constancy). One cannot arise without the other.

If the appearance of something approaches a pure (geometrical) form, as the still surface of a lake does, we become particularly sensitive to the finest perturbations, such as are summoned on the lake by a breath of air. Our capacity to identify with the context of transformation, that is, to experience change and constancy at the same time, allows us to experience metamorphoses in our thinking, and out of this experience to arrange the different appearances sequentially.

*

We have described acquiescence and receptiveness as characteristics of the air element. The air may buffet us as wind or storm, but its essential nature is to be the bearer of something else—water, light, warmth or sound—and only thereby become perceptible to the senses. To determine the direction of the wind, we look at a tree or a weathercock. Our own air, our breath, does its work best when we do not notice it. If we do notice our breathing, it means some organic disturbance exists (unless we are deliberately observing it).

If this characteristic of air becomes an inner activity in us, it leads to enhanced attentiveness, to "directed receptiveness." It may also be called an attitude of questioning with respect to what we perceive.[21] Among the most significant experiences of the "airy" mode of observation, is the experience of the "sucking" of the question in perception. The greater this force is, the more richly the answers can flow to us. We thereby feel that our thinking activity is connected with something which *illuminates* the interrelationship of the appearances of our surroundings. With the help of this illuminating element, we see the momentary spatial interrelationship of the different appearances. Here we shall call this the *"context of appearances."*

★

That which comes to us from outside as an element, and that with which we feel inwardly connected as active human beings—these two sides come closest together in the experience of warmth. We experience how the element of warmth in the world permeates, energizes or overwhelms us. But we also feel ourselves *united with this energizing activity*—we feel fired with ideas as we strive to penetrate the contextual relationships of the world.

★

Thus we find in our thinking four modes of experiencing the contextual relationships of the world. If we become aware of them, and use them as organs for perceiving the world, we bring ourselves in relation to the activity of the periphery. In this way, thinking as an organ of perception can give us access to the different layers of the etheric world:

1. Through our own all-permeating activity of thinking, through trying to comprehend contextual relationships, we become aware of the energizing nature of the warmth-effects in the world. The idea manifests in the world as will: *Warmth Ether.*

2. With the illuminating power of thinking, which makes the contextual relationships apparent, we find our way to the context of appearances, to the light-like working of the world which is imparted to us through space. As wisdom-filled context, the idea becomes an image: *Light Ether.*

3. The inwardly progressive, systematizing activity of thinking leads us to the context of transformation, to the activity of the world which works rhythmically, resonantly or chemically in the flow of time. The idea becomes active in systematizing and transforming the material: *Chemical or Sound Ether.*

4. That which lives and works in us as concept, as the shadow of a living being, links us with the context of life, with the meaningful activity of a being. The idea is individualized as a completed entity: *Meaning or Life Ether.*

Warmth as Element and Ether

As described in the previous section, warmth experienced outwardly, as an element, is usually related to our activity of discovering contextual relationships; conversely, as an ether, as an activity of the periphery, warmth is so to speak centralized within us. Thus it is difficult to make a sharp distinction between these two modes of activity. Warmth as element and warmth as etheric activity thus become two aspects of *one* mode of observation; this mode brings to experience the origin of a being's "beingness" [*Wesenhaftes in seinem Ursprung*].

What is meant here can be illustrated with a *seed*. The outer appearance of the seed has little to offer us, but this dark and dry shell is nevertheless the point upon which all our cognitive activity is concentrated. Within the seed we could find the little embryo, but we cannot examine it further if we are to retain a seed out of which a plant can later grow.

In *bloom* the Peony reveals its whole being; it asks to be apprehended as an externally perceptible picture. Its specific spiritual formative activity has completely opened itself to the outside, to the periphery. There is no more developmental potential in what the plant offers to the senses. It will die back.

In the seed, the opposite condition prevails. Its reality lies primarily in that which we do not see. We realize the direction we must take in order to experience its reality: We must have followed the outer development of the plant and learned to know its possibilities and limitations of development. If we then make this process of development alive in us—now without regard to outer appearances—we find we have the ability to let any possible form arise out of the seed. It then forms itself in us, according to the conditions we impose each time in our thinking. This process is a reflection of the influences mediated by the etheric.

Thus, in considering the seed-condition of the plant, we must to a large degree renounce everything "actual" and, by melting together our mental pictures of particular appearances, create the germ's condition of potentiality, i.e. the *impulse to germinate*. In this impulse we find warmth

Illus. 1. Flowering Peony (wild form of *Paeonia officinalis*).

Second year
Summer

Winter

Third year
Summer

Winter

Illus. 2 (pp. 40–45). Development of a Peony over six years from seedling to fruit formation; grown in the earth in a root observation box (40×100×10cm).

Peony. Fourth year, summer.   *Winter*

Peony. Fifth year, summer.   *Sixth year, winter.*

42

Peony. Sixth year. Development of the first flowering shoot.

Illus. 3. Overwintering bud of a Peony; right, with protective leaves removed.

Peony. Sixth year. Flowering and fruiting shoots.

Illus. 4. Dissected overwintering bud from Illus. 3. Complete series of leaves and leaf primordia for the following year's growth (including the primordium of the flower bud).

First spring.   *Second spring.*

Illus. 7 (pp. 48–52). Development of a Stinking Hellebore from seedling to fruit formation. In the first autumn transplanted from the wild and grown in the earth in a root observation box (80 × 120 × 10cm).

◄◄◄
Illus. 5 (p. 46). Site of an old clearing in a beech forest in the Jura mountains (limestone) with a thick growth of large Stinking Hellebore plants and southeastern exposure (compare Illus. 8, above).

◄◄
Illus. 6 (p. 47). Lightly wooded site on a steep southern slope a few years after the underbrush was destroyed by fire. Only a few of the small but mature Stinking Hellebore plants have begun to flower (compare Illus. 8, below).

49

Hellebore. September.   *November.*

50

Hellebore. Beginning of January.

February. Flowering and fruiting plant. ▶

51

Illus. 8. Hellebore. Mature flowering plants from two sites: above, from the site in Illus. 5 (p. 46); below, from the site in Illus. 6 (p. 47).

53

Illus. 9. Flowering Hellebore (*Helleborus foetidus*).

54

activity. We can observe how the innate potentialities of a *being* flow into a *process*: whether in a cool way, or energetically, or with such excessive force that it destroys its own forms. Hence, in relation to the elements in the surroundings, warmth can work either as a builder or a destroyer. It reveals itself in the intensity of the processes.

The Context of Appearances—Light Ether

When we turn to that which is revealed to our senses, and bring to life in our thinking the contextual relationship of the appearances of our surroundings, we then experience the activity of the light ether.[22]

The interrelationship of appearances in the present constitutes the light ether. It comes to us through all our senses, but particularly through sight. We apprehend it by allowing it to become an inner picture for us. Previously we attended to the way the interplay of the elements expresses itself *in the plant*. Now, by observing the context of appearances, we learn to see how this interplay fits itself into an environment *through a plant*. We see how a group of trees grows into a whole which mirrors in detail the light conditions of a particular place. We see the contrast and interpenetration of light and darkness in a particular situation: light that awakens the manifold appearances of the world, and darkness that lacks light and to various degrees yearns for light. We can trace a progression:

In *darkened* surroundings a herbaceous plant develops pale transparent shoots, without leaves or flowers; it is a picture of the yearning for light. Similar forms occur in the root, where the plant actively turns to the darkness and connects itself with the earth.

In *shady* surroundings, a uniform greeness arises, with pale inconspicuous flowers and dim unspecific odors.

A *sunny* place makes a colorful picture. The colors of the

plants are enhanced. They show many differentiated hues and forms, and have characteristic scents. They express themselves more specifically, yet always in relation to their particular situation.[23]

The appearances vary according to the temperature, the moisture, and the soil conditions. Thus, as we did with light and darkness, we can also consider within the context of appearances the relation of the plant to the environment from the aspects of warm-cold, dry-moist and lush-sparse. In a given situation, the activities of the elements unite to form a *single* pictorial appearance.[24]

In this mode of observation we experience how the appearance of the blooming Peony (Illus. 1) unites intensive growth with glowing color. The voluptuous red flowers burst out of the lush, red-tinged green of the foliage. The blooming Peony makes a picture of the conditions we can experience in the open woods and meadows of a south-facing mountain slope that is moist, warm and sunny.

In contrast, the Stinking Hellebore (Illus. 9) conjures up a picture of a sunny but cool situation in a protected place, at the edge of a beech forest, with favorable, not too dry soil.

The Context of Transformation—Sound Ether

The context of appearances is not stationary; sunshine alternates with rain, day with night, summer with winter. We cannot stay with the currently prevailing sense impression; we need the help of our memory to recognize the context of this alternation.

Also these occurrences are pictured in the plant. Just as on an overcast day its appearance retains for a while the picture of a sunny day, so does its whole form retain in the present, pictures of its past development. The present appearance is the result of a process in time which we can bring to life again with pictorial thinking.

Thus, the present appearance of the plant points to its past. We recognize the coherence in the transformation. The present picture, however, cannot fully reveal the transformational context. We must also as it were "hear" the course of the year as a harmonious unity within the specific developmental pattern of a herbaceous plant, or within the branching pattern of a tree.

In this way, the plant becomes an expression of how the relationships of the elements have changed during a definite period of time, how a particular site has changed its appearance. Although it can differ with each individual plant, every species has its own particular relationship to the environment. To a certain extent it can adapt, but if it does not succeed, it is replaced by another species.

The pictures of the flowering Peony and Stinking Hellebore described in the previous section make a strong impression on us. They can be grasped in terms of the momentary context of appearances, but they also point beyond this spatial context to a sequence in time:

The first picture speaks of the culmination of the first half of the year, the "ascending" part. Bursting out of a rounded, long-prepared bud, the colored blossom of the Peony remains connected in its way with the burgeoning growth of the entire plant. In this picture a particular segment of the cycle of the year is revealed: the warmth and light that are present have emerged from a cool and damp winter and are striving toward a warm and dry summertime in which the soil still retains its moisture.

The other picture is more restrained. An unusual winter verdancy, emerging as if from the depths of the plant, itself begins to flower. Against the dark green of the over-wintering foliage and the brown surroundings, the light green inflorescence of the Stinking Hellebore makes just as "colorful" a contrast in February as the Peony does in summer.

If in this way we observe the different plant species growing next to one another—how they bloom one after the other, each in its own manner—we gradually come to perceive what we may call the "expression of the earth" ["*Mimik der Erde*"].[25]

The Context of Life—Life Ether

As with the elements, we need to find in each of the different layers of the etheric a certain completeness, we need to encompass each of them as a self-contained realm, and we need to find their limits. In so doing, the realm which a particular mode of observation opens up to us then becomes surveyable. At the same time, one increasingly notices experiences which point further, and call for a new mode of observation.

If we consider the *context of appearances*, a clear limit is given where the immediate perception of the present ceases. The context which we are aware of through our senses has its own completeness, and indeed we are able for a time to concentrate on this exclusively.

With the context of appearances, one lives into the pictorial quality of the phenomenal world; one brings calm and surveyability to one's perceptions through inner thought activity. One's attention is directed toward completing a picture and toward bringing, along with what can be seen, the consciousness of the ideal circle of relations that belong to the visible things.

Thus the present is grasped in a timeless, pictorial fashion. But as soon as one attends to the fact that the present appearances also live in a stream of time and everywhere hint at processes of becoming, the mode of observation has already changed. The attention is then directed to the *context of transformation*—that is, the present appearances are seen in relation to others which we find in our memory.

In grasping the context of transformation and moving

from one picture to another, the order-creating activity of rhythm is experienced. The individual pictures appear and disappear like the tones of a melody. The background for this is the capacity to experience rhythm as a connected whole, particularly the rhythm of the course of the year in all its phases. Here attention is directed to the effort to create a concordance between the fluctuation of the feelings and the changes of the outer appearances, and thus to bring the rhythmic process of the world to sound out from within ourselves.

The development of the plant is revealed as embedded in the seasons of the year. With its help, we awaken in ourselves a specific aspect of the course of the year, a musical concord of successive experiences.

There are still other experiences beyond this awareness of a rhythmic, self-renewing order in the dying and becoming of nature; only through these does what has already been described really become an "earthly" experience. They point to the level of the *"life context."*

The context of life gives a kernel of stability to the changing appearances. The fact that despite years of change we continue to recognize a particular tree or place individually, and may even give it a name, shows that we have begun to be acquainted with its particular life history, and to see this within the present appearances.

*

Let us look at a clearing which was made a few years ago in a tall forest of beech, oak, maple and ash (Illus. 5). It is on a south slope and is protected from wind on all sides. On the very fertile forest floor above the limestone of the Jura mountains, a lush growth of green plants has developed. If we visit it in late winter, we find large areas covered by the abundant dark green growth of the Stinking Hellebore with its many broad and much-branched inflorescences (see Illus. 8 above). Interspersed are large bushes of Spurge, which are preparing to create a similar picture a little later on. This will suffice as an indication of the situation.

One reaches the kind of experience under consideration here, only if it is possible to live with such a place and familiarize oneself with its life over a longer period of time. Then one begins to see in the broad rhythms of the seasons of the year, in the succession of plant communities, in the geological and geographical circumstances of the place, and in the purposeful actions of human beings, how all these form a living whole; one sees how through these a being is able to develop a certain independence here on the earth.

In such a place even an individual Hellebore plant acquires a quite different character from another growing nearby, for instance on the steep south-facing slope of a low beech and pine forest with little undergrowth and poor stony soil (Illus. 6). There, at the same season, we find some very small Hellebore plants (Illus. 8 below) with small, somewhat red-tinged leaves. Some years ago, fire destroyed the ground cover at this spot. Immediately afterwards, these plants germinated. A seedling taken from there by the author and planted in more favorable conditions, grew within one and half years into a large, abundantly flowering plant. Those remaining, however, grew very slowly and only began to flower five years later, at which time they were still quite little.

In this manner, we can trace how the present conditions of a place and the rhythmic changes of the year, punctuated with certain more traumatic events, work together in the plants at these two sites. We can also follow how the plants develop individually from year to year. Everything that happens at a place leaves an impression. It is true that the effects of a small fire are soon overgrown, and cannot be directly seen after a while, but they nevertheless persist in an altered form. The fact that small Hellebore plants are now growing at this site, and that they are all of the same age, is one of the surely numerous unexpected consequences that can only be understood at the level of the context of life.

Here we can only indicate that it is possible to delve still further into that which we look for within ourselves: we can recognize that we are seeking the elemental beings operative in nature. The more these beings manifest in outer appearance (for instance in summer), the more they are "bound"; they are "liberated" when they live as possibilities in the environmental circumstances of a particular place (as they do in winter). Generally, however, they live in the world in a state of enchantment (i.e. "bound"); we break the enchantment insofar as we recognize their activity in the world. They arise and decay with nature, and thus their conditions of life can easily be destroyed by human beings.

Summary: The Connection of Terrestrial and Cosmic Activity

In the way here described, the elements and the ethers mediate in distinct ways between what is given by the physical sense world, and what is inwardly experienced of the periphery, the cosmos.

The *elements* come to our attention through the senses. They are at first sense phenomena. We can allow these phenomena to become a picture for us, and can then gradually discover within ourselves the forces that underlie them. We can learn to work consciously with these forces in reading the "text" of nature.

Etheric activity, in contrast, first enters our consciousness as distinct modes of pictorial experience. We start with the experience of thinking. Only gradually do we gain access through this to the activity of the cosmic periphery in the sense world around us (the "context" of nature). Thus, we only truly experience etheric activity when we no longer merely think it and experience it in thinking, but rather use thinking to actually find it in the world.

If we direct ourselves by these means toward the plant, or some other natural object, we come to know it through the *elements* in a fourfold way, insofar as it is a terrestrial being. The levels of the *etheric*, in contrast, show us to what degree such a being has been formed out of the context of the cosmos, how it continues to live within this context, and how through it a particular cosmic aspect manifests itself on earth. Thus, the layers of the elements and the ethers become the means for understanding the physical and cosmic aspects of the world around us. We do not grasp the context of the world through single factors or even the positions of stars— we grasp it through relationships. Through what we read in the picture of the plant, we become aware of that which works in relationships of wholeness. Since the plant world itself participates in the surroundings and helps shape these, the elemental and etheric modes of observation naturally interpenetrate here.

If we look at the relationship between the elements and the ethers, we can see how through earth and water the terrestrial activity proper comes to expression, and how through light and warmth the terrestrial is incorporated into the cosmic activity. Correspondingly, warmth and light mediate the etheric cosmic activity directly, while at the level of the chemical and life ethers, cosmic activity becomes incorporated into terrestrial activity.[26]

The etheric as such only becomes perceptible to us in its effects, when it takes on form in some way. This form is fixed in the solid element. As such, however, it originates from a higher level. What is specific in the form, what we experience as its essential content, this speaks on different levels to our soul. Already by the way we grasp it, it shows itself to be related to the soul world, the astral world.[27] Thus it is quite justified to maintain that in speaking of formative forces we cannot confine ourselves exclusively to the level of the etheric. The latter is the level of contextual activity. That which is revealed through the formative forces can indeed be grasped and described as a pictorial interplay of activities, but this interplay as such is only a picture of a being of the astral world which is revealing itself through it. This world is accessible only to a stage of cognition that extends beyond Imaginative (pictorial) consciousness.[28]

As we grasp the elements in succession, from earth through water to air and warmth, it is evident that we are nearing the archetypes of the beings of nature at the level of the etheric. It is as if we were making a link with the past, with the origin of the beings of nature. As we go further, to the observational modes of light, sound and life, we notice how from the opposite side we are once again nearing the reality of terrestrial life. We learn what germinal potentials lie concealed in the archetypes that have been actualized. This leads us into the future, and helps us fit our own deeds into the context of nature.

Normally, when we want to be active in the world, we allow ourselves to be guided by thoughts which concern only that portion of the world that interests us directly. We believe we have the full picture if we know the effects of our actions as we know those of a machine, and therefore understand how to obtain the necessary materials. With this, however, we are not yet fully conscious of reality. For when we really do act, or do use the machine, and thereby bring our ideas to be active within the various layers of the world which we have described, we suddenly discover that our actions have unexpected repercussions. Our activities have disturbed nature's context of appearances, context of transformation and context of life. We expect, as a matter of course, that nature will put things back in order. She does so in her own way, but as we have not sought access to her ways, they remain incomprehensible to us.

If we school our thinking on the contextual relationships of our surroundings, then, to the extent that undisturbed nature reveals itself in our thinking, we are ever more able to bring our actions into harmony with the processes of nature. We learn to help nature to develop a future which she is indeed predisposed for, but which she cannot attain by herself. If one lets an oak tree grow naturally in the woods, it conforms to the other trees and makes a long un-branched trunk. Man can consciously promote this form of growth. Or he can arrange that the oak grow freestanding and thereby allow it to assume its own predisposed shape. Without man's intervention, a forest would have grown up around it.

On the other hand, a quite different impulse is at work when, for instance through pruning, we try to force a tree into a specific shape which does not correspond to its natu-ral form of growth. We find then that all kinds of difficulties arise which counteract our intentions.

In earlier times, these matters were taken care of by in-stinct or tradition. Today, our knowledge is focussed on the separate details. We are guided by pictures of finished things, and from these we construct the pictures of the future we desire. But we conceive these pictures in the same way as those of the past. Our way of thinking is not ade-quate to the future. For the development of ecology, agri-culture, the cultivation of medicinal plants, etc., it will matter increasingly that we penetrate through the experi-ences of the past to a grasp of the archetypes, and that through this our intentions for the future be given a direc-tion which is in accordance with the spiritual cosmos.

When we strive to become truly responsible for our actions in this way, we do not determine the consequences of these actions beforehand. However, as the capacity grows in us to survey the contextual relationships of nature as a whole, as described here, we can have confidence that what is right will occur, if we maintain our efforts and our attention toward becoming more responsible.

Notes

The plates and illustrations for this paper originate in the work of the Research Laboratory at the Goetheanum, Dornach, Switzerland. Illustrations 1 and 9 are reproduced from paintings by Alexandra Beresford.

References to untranslated works of Rudolf Steiner are given by GA number (GA = Gesamtausgabe = Collected Edition, published by Rudolf Steiner Verlag, Dornach).

1. Steiner, Rudolf. *The Philosophy of Freedom* (1894). Spring Valley, N.Y.: Anthroposophic Press 1964. See esp. chapters 4 and 5.

2. Goethe, Johann Wolfgang von. "The Objective and Subjective Reconciled by Means of the Experiment" (1793) in *Goethe's Botanical Writings*. Honolulu: University of Hawaii Press 1952.

3. Steiner, R. *Practical Training in Thought* (1909). Spring Valley, N.Y.: Anthroposophic Press 1974. (Single lecture.)

4. Maier, Georg. "Die Elemente als Stufen der Naturbetrachtung." *Elemente der Naturwissenschaft* 13(1970):1-9.

5. See Steiner, R. *Theosophy* (1904). Spring Valley, N.Y.: Anthroposophic Press 1971. Chapter 3, sections 1 and 2.

6. Steiner, R. *Anthroposophical Leading Thoughts* (1924-1925). London: Rudolf Steiner Press 1973. Article of March 8, 1925. Also Steiner, R., and Ita Wegman. *Fundamentals of Therapy* (1925). 4th ed. London: Rudolf Steiner Press 1983. Chapter 2.

7. Steiner, R. *Anthroposophical Leading Thoughts* (1925). London: Rudolf Steiner Press 1973. Article of February 1, 1925.

8. Steiner, R. and I. Wegman. *Fundamentals of Therapy* (1925). 4th ed. London: Rudolf Steiner Press 1983. Chapter 2.

9. Compare Rudolf Steiner, *Das Sonnenmysterium und das Mysterium von Tod und Auferstehung* (1922). GA 211, 1963. Lecture of June 11, 1922. See also

Steiner, R. *Warmth Course* (1920). Spring Valley, N.Y.: Mercury Press 1980. Lecture of March 2, 1920.

10. Steiner, R. *Karmic Relationships*, vol. 3 (1924). London: Rudolf Steiner Press 1977. Lecture of August 1, 1924.

11. Steiner, R. *Mathematik, Wissenschaftliches Experiment, Beobachtung und Erkenntnisergebnisse vom Gesichtspunkt der Anthroposophie* (1921). GA 324, 2nd ed. 1972. Lecture of March 19, 1921. Steiner, R. *Esoteric Development: Selected Lectures and Writings from the Works of Rudolf Steiner.* Spring Valley, N.Y.: Anthroposophic Press 1982. Chapter 2. See also statements about independent thoughts in the lecture of Rudolf Steiner of December 31, 1922, contained in *Man and the World of the Stars* (1922), Spring Valley, N.Y.: Anthroposophic Press 1963.

12. Steiner, R. *Lebendiges Naturerkennen. Intellektueller Sündenfall und spirituelle Sündenerhebung* (1923). GA 220, 2nd ed. 1982. Lectures of January 19 & 20, 1923.

13. See note 4.

14. See the essay "Streaming: A Picture of the Etheric" in this book (p. 91ff.).

15. Splechtner, F.J.N. "Goethes Gesetz der Metamorphose und die Regel von den sogenannten homologen Variationsserien." *Gäa Sophia* 5(1930):118ff.

16. See the essay "The Formative Movements of Plants" in this book (p. 131ff.) for details on how such formative movements may be found and what laws of the time-body may be read from these.

17. Bockemühl, Jochen. "Staubblatt und Fruchtblatt." *Elemente der Naturwissenschaft* 13(1970):12-24.

18. Schad, Wolfgang. "Friedrich Siegmund Voigt und Albert Wigand." *Elemente der Naturwissenschaft* 10(1969): 48-49.

19. See Maier, Georg. "Zum Begriff der Trübe." *Elemente der Naturwissenschaft* 19(1973):1-12.

20. Grohmann, Gerbert. *Die Pflanze: Ein Weg zum Verständnis ihres Wesens* vol. 2 (1951). 3rd ed. Stuttgart: Verlag Freies Geistesleben 1981. Page 35ff.

21. Steiner, R. *A Theory of Knowledge Implicit in Goethe's World Conception* (1886). Spring Valley, N.Y.: Anthroposophic Press 1968. See chapter 11.

22. See the next essay, by Georg Maier.

23. Bockemühl, J. "Lichtwirksamkeit im Bild der Pflanzenentwicklung." *Elemente der Naturwissenschaft* 25(1976):9-12.

24. See note 1 of the following essay (p. 88).

25. Steiner, R. *Occult Reading and Occult Hearing* (1914). London: Rudolf Steiner Press 1975. Lecture of October 5, 1914.

26. Compare Steiner, R. *Agriculture Course* (1924). London: Bio-Dynamic Agricultural Assoc. 1974. Lectures of June 7 & 10, 1924.

27. Compare the description of the different regions of the soul world in R. Steiner's *Theosophy* (see note 5).

28. See note 11.

Light and the Pictorial Appearance of the World

Georg Maier

At the break of day, sunlight gently spreads over the earth. Single objects begin to emerge from the darkness of the landscape; we know they are but part of a whole which we cannot yet fully take in. It is the activity of light that brings them together, weaving them at last into an illuminated scene. Landscape and sky merge into a meaningful picture.[1] The present essay sets out to draw attention to a number of phenomena where such "pictorial" relationships can be studied. We will attempt to develop an adequate mode of observing such relationships and also consider their human significance.

In the glittering images of the sun on a moving surface of water, we recognize that the luminosity of the sky is being reflected. Or when the spatial form of a tree is underlined by the play of light and shade, we recognize how our wider surroundings are "reflected" in a single detail of the scene. Our activity of thinking is necessary in order to grasp relationships of this kind. In our cognitive activity we ourselves weave the threads—which in themselves are invisible—between the phenomena.[2]

Light too shares in this weaving, mediating function. Insofar as we mean by "light" an activity which blends the phenomena of the world into a totality accessible to our thinking, we may refer to it as "light ether."[3] In the tradition of ancient Greece, the ether is a sphere of brilliant luminosity spread out over the earth. Pallas Athene leaves the earth and goes

"Into Olympus, which is called the eternal seat of
    the Gods,
Which storms cannot shake, nor rains deluge,
Nor even snow overtake; there the ether's shimmer-
    ing brightness
Spreads without cloud and covers the mount with
    radiant brilliance,
Where day by day the blessed Gods live in joy."[4]

Let us return to the morning twilight. Before day takes
hold of the earth we rely on our body's sense of touch, a
sense which depends on direct physical contact. In the dark
we experience the appearance and disappearance of the
touch perceptions. By means of these we comprehend the
area surrounding our physical body. With the light, our
world expands to far distances and great heights. In the
space between near and far objects there always remains a
hint of the space between the earth and the ether sphere, as
the latter is called in the poem above.

Spatial Differentiation in the Visible World

On all sides we are surrounded by the visible world. To
be sure, at first we see no more than our limited field of vision can take in, and of this, strictly speaking, we see only a
small area with any great clarity. And yet, the different sec-
tors fit together seamlessly to become a panorama on the
horizon, a celestial dome in the heights. We can establish an
awareness of the *totality of our surroundings* through a pictorial conceptualization of the whole. The visible world is
organized to form a unity.

Moreover, we are accustomed to add to our surroundings the dimension of depth, which we regard as an objective and integral part of the totality. A consideration of the
very different ways in which this spatial depth dimension

comes to expression can help us to become aware of our life in the world of visible phenomena.

If we are out of doors in the daylit landscape, we take in with our gaze the whole of the space which is spread out between ourselves and the horizon. In our immediate vicinity the eye is confronted with a variety of grasses and other plants, with their leaves and flowers. If we raise our eyes, these details merge together and become—a meadow. Here we can distinguish details on a larger scale, perhaps some fruit trees, but at somewhat greater distances these too give way to the overall form of trees. Still more distant trees may blend into a forest, whose "textures" betray where firs, or deciduous trees, predominate. The differentiation of the landscape into hills and mountains may follow, whereby an increasingly uniform coloration begins to spread over large areas of land. The distant horizon connects the earth and the sky. On the scale we have characterized, quite different things become apparent at different distances. It is by no means a foregone conclusion that we can observe an object best from close up. A mountain which we have observed from the distance is no longer recognizable when viewed from its own peak; indeed, its form is often not visible at all. Distance may thus offer a new phenomena, which cannot be seen from close proximity.

Within the two dimensions of pictorial phenomena, the dimension of depth comes about through various forms of perspective. The so-called linear perspective brings about, as it were, a connection between the space we can encompass with our bodily movements, and the size relationships in the space we can only grasp visually. Take an avenue of equally spaced trees stretching out into the distance, whose uniform width could be paced out at any point. This picture is often used as a symbolic expression for the decreasing size of objects seen at increasing distances. In the distance the avenue contracts into a point. This illustrates only one aspect of reality, namely the disappearance of tangible things with increasing distance. The distance is actually filled with differentiated objects of vision—only these cannot be correlated with tangible objects of human dimensions.[5]

When we walk with our gaze directed straight ahead, we experience how individual objects become larger, sometimes even growing beyond our field of vision. Once we have passed them, we will occasionally glance back at an object that is dwindling in size. When we gaze in the direction in which we are walking, we notice that the *size relationships* of the surroundings change. Distance means that things have a relatively constant apparent size; nearness means that an object "reacts" to a small movement on our part with a considerable change of size. We free ourselves from the stereotyped concept of the avenue by taking this movement into account. The distance remains in the picture as the unifying frame of our surroundings. Images of tangible objects grow out of this frame and again disappear into it.

The picture of the landscape changes in another way if we direct our gaze toward the side of our path. Our closest surroundings are in constant flux, the objects remain with us only briefly; the distance, on the other hand, accompanies and moves with us as it were. The objects turn themselves, they show different sides to us. In this way, the relationship "in front/behind" dominates the spatial order of things. A more distant object disappears behind a nearer one, and reappears on the other side. In the case of ordinary opaque bodies this means that the one covers and obscures the other. The transformation of the landscape for a gaze lateral to the direcion of movement is thus not one of relative sizes, but of *relative positions*. (On a smaller scale, this also determines the difference between the images seen by the right and the left eye: the impression of spatial depth in binocular vision arises from the different spatial orientations of the eyes.) This form of experiencing depth is fundamentally different from that of perspective, described above. Most optical instruments, as well as pictures projected onto screens, make the judgment of distance by perspective difficult to reconcile with the effects, say, of stereoscopy.[6]

We have thus far considered inferences about the mutual position and size of objects. We now come to their color. When the air is hazy or misty, we are surrounded by a space in which the foreground stands out against the background by virtue of the intensity of color and the sharpness of contour. In passing from close to distant objects, the contrasts are lost and the entire periphery tends at last toward a uniform grey. The air can also create a *color perspective* if it is just slightly turbid. In this case the distance becomes a bluish darkness or a reddish brightness, depending on the conditions. In these tones, little of the pigmentary surface color of things can be distinguished. Brightness softened to a reddish tone indicates a shining, as of snow-covered peaks, whereas the bluish shimmering air only appears in front of dark shadows. A depth dimension is created which is not measured in steps. It consists rather of a scale in which sense qualities gradually change their significance: they range from the localized pigmentary colors to the colors of the sky, which express the interrelationship of characteristic factors like the position of the sun, the compass direction, the weather conditions, etc.

In comparing the special possibilities which we have considered for comprehending the depth of an image, a certain order begins to emerge:

1. *Positional perspective in the visual surroundings*
   The world appears spatially tangible when we have the opportunity to regard things now from one side, now from

the other. Triangulation in land surveying rests upon this principle. With its help we can project into the world measurements of length which we would normally only be able to comprehend by pacing them off. In this context, distance is that part of our surroundings which accompanies us as we move, remaining relatively unchanged.

2. *Size perspective in the visual surroundings*
   When we approach an object, its apparent size begins to increase, it begins to occupy a greater portion of our surroundings. This observation of the apparent expansion and contraction of objects leads us to recognize them as being "objects of vision." We know that the brightness at a particular place is determined by the brightness of the sky overhead. If we approach a lamp it becomes brighter, inasmuch as it appears larger and assumes a greater part of our visual field. There are, however, objects of vision which assume a definite and individual size in the visual field. The rainbow is an example. It makes no difference whether it appears in the (physically) distant rainfall or in the (physically) nearby scattered water-drops of a garden hose: it remains the same size in relation to our field of vision. (Similarly, with regard to positional perspective, it parallels our wanderings like an infinitely distant object).

3. *Atmospheric perspective*
   All color is a sense quality for the eye, and is as such intangible. Color perspective is based on shades of coloration which indicate the relative distances of things: nearby objects have clear and definite colors, distant ones have luminous colors that blend into the ethereal color of the sky. Even in the intense blue coloration of many bodies of water, we are in fact dealing with something intangible. Indeed, the rich and saturated colors of unusually large precious stones can easily be misinterpreted as

a special property inherent in the material itself.[7] The colors which fill space are fundamentally different in quality from those which appear in space outwardly, i.e. on surfaces. We feel ourselves directly engaged in the inwardness of the colors of the sky around us. It becomes meaningful to connect their sensory-moral expression, as Goethe called it, with the "gesture" of their mode of origin in our overall experience.

From the Object to the Image:
The World Seen Through the Prism

We are used to regarding the visible things around us as tangible objects. Indeed, we can watch how we are naturally inclined to run our hand along a visible edge. The color we see proves to be dependent on the nature of the material—we speak of pigments. In the preceding section we have seen how this direct association of visible things with tangible objects is no longer experienced at greater distances. For the eye, the world increasingly takes on the character of a pure image.

Prisms of solid glass or hollow prisms filled with water give us the possibility of looking into a visual world less closely connected with our tangible surroundings than is otherwise the case. An intensive play of colors arises which does not allow us to grasp at the objects so seen in our accustomed way. We speak of spectra ("phantoms")—visible phenomena which cannot be touched like material bodies. All the same, though position, form and color may be altered, we are able to recognize the objects that are immediately visible. It is on and around them that the colors arise. Along the clearly contrasted edges of a window-pane, highly luminous edges of red-yellow and blue-violet appear. Moreover, if we observe carefully the arrangement of the colors on these edges, we see how the red-yellow and the blue-violet stripes stand in opposition, as it were—for instance on the upper and lower edges of a bright surface. This same order prevails throughout the field of vision. A series of dark bars on a light background will show the same sequence of colors on the upper edge of each bar. This arrangement is dependent on the orientation of the prism. If we turn it so that its edges are no longer horizontal, but vertical, the bands of color will also move into the vertical. At the same time, the whole image is displaced to one side, compared to that given by direct vision. These few indications may suffice for the time being to stimulate the reader to carry out his own observations. Two things are essential in this connection: Firstly, it is just that part of the phenomenon which eludes the sense of touch, namely the arrangement of the colors, that proves to be governed by a general law, applicable to all parts of the image. Secondly, it is through the contrasts in brightness that the colors arise; the color is not attached to the material objects—it rather demarcates the outlines, the transitions, the mutual relationships.

This was the startling discovery which Goethe describes as the initial stimulus to his decades-long study of color phenomena. Within a uniformly bright surface, no color can arise; the colors gather instead around spots, edges, reflections and similar irregularities. Accordingly, Goethe constructed cards with specially arranged patterns in black and white, by means of which the laws governing the color sequences could be clearly demonstrated.[8]

In the moment of looking through a prism, a specific lawful orderliness is, as it were, imposed upon the visible world. It can be discovered in the mutual relationships of the individual objects of perception. The image seen through a prism becomes indistinct in detail, and withdraws from the realm of tangible objectivity. By looking through a prism we can prepare ourselves to heed the context of the world's visible appearances also in other situations.

The Context of Appearances and the Direction of Illumination
    As the sun rises over the horizon, the character of the landscape undergoes a fundamental change. The contrasts of light and darkness become at once richer and more defined. They are all orientated in the direction of the sun. The phenomenon to which we refer can best be studied by letting our gaze wander through our surroundings. Let us, for example, choose a direction in which the objects are illuminated from the side. The sun is now shining toward one side of our body; we may even feel its warmth on our cheek. The illuminated part of every tree faces the same direction. Just as we are able to find a new law, superimposed on a set of phenomena when we look through a prism, so here too the clear sunlight spreads over the landscape a single, overarching principle, which light and darkness always follow. In lateral illumination the spatial differentiation, the sculptural nature of the objects, becomes especially pronounced. In such light the regular alternation of bright and dark contours can reveal the presence of an otherwise well-concealed fossil on a cliff-face, and on aerial photographs taken when the sun is low, the slightest undulations of the ground may appear in sharp relief, indicating perhaps the foundation-lines of an ancient settlement. We will always find that the *one* sun belongs equally to the near and distant objects; light from behind the object, light from the side, or light from behind the viewer—in each direction all the objects appear in a different but unified manner. (Conversely, we can also direct our attention to a single plant, and by encircling it, experience all the constellations of the sunlight.[9])
    As soon as we look directly away from the sun, the shadows disappear, with the result that our view of the world loses its depth; the objects appear as though on the flat surface of a mosaic. A kind of hazy luminosity spreads over the landscape and the details become indistinct. But the sun is

now behind us, and we have escaped its direct brilliance.

Some most remarkable effects can be observed in a back-lit landscape. At first the earthly surroundings are virtually obliterated from view by the sun's radiance. Only by shading our eyes, and so looking out from the darkness beneath our hand, can we discover further phenomena. The strong contrasts between the shaded sides of the objects facing us, and the brilliance shining around their silhouetted outlines, does not bring out the sculptural quality of their forms. Their colors too tend to be obscured in the glittering that arises on surface features such as hairs, and on areas that are especially glossy. Even the air becomes filled with an inner radiance. Haze, insects and the finest dust become clearly visible near the sun. For this reason, the details of a mountainous terrain take on an especially clear three-dimensional quality through the sequence of dark outlines and the hazy brightness that issues from the valleys between them. (Much more could be said about the appearances of the landscape when the sun is low; these things first emerge when the qualitative differences of the direction of illumination are taken into account.)

The more intensively we familiarize ourselves through observation and thinking with light's quality of creating coherent scenes, the richer in detail and in gesture will the pictures in our memory become. Above all, our mental pictures will no longer be restricted to a few seemingly important grey details. For in fact, our mental pictures are always the product of our mode of thinking and observation.

As objects of vision, the phenomena observed in sunlight belong to a larger context. In this context every detail is borne by its surroundings. Relative brightness changes throughout the course of the day, and develops each day in accordance with the place and with the season. If only we observe in the right way, we will discover that under any

weather conditions the visible objects are an image or reflection of their surroundings. Even in the diffuse, all-around
light of a fog, a curious phenomenon develops: in the interior of a patch of shrubbery the darkness seems to draw itself together. Flower petals turned outwards appear whitish,
while between the successive layers of petals in an open
corolla the colors become ever more saturated toward the inside. Once again, the picture the plant presents fits in per-
fectly with the prevailing illumination of the surroundings.

The integrating activity of the sunlight embraces near
and distant objects alike. The context of appearances of the
distance—the ether-sphere of the Greeks—also embraces
our immediate surroundings. A sense for this reality can be
schooled through quite simple daily observations. To illustrate, let us consider the appearance of our own hand. Quite
apart from the fact that we see it in the most manifold forms
and gestures—open, spread, clenched into a fist—its appearance is also an expression of the particular illumination in
which it is seen. Depending on how we turn it, the play of
light and darkness, sheen and shadow, brings forth new images, in which quite different properties can come to expression. This can be tried before a bright window or in direct
sunlight. The spatial form becomes strongly evident if every
finger and every raised part on the surface of the hand is
emphasized through the lightening of one side and the dark-
ening of the other. The condition for this is lateral illumination. Next we can turn our back to the sun. As we do so, the
hand increasingly loses its shadow, its own color becomes
brighter and we notice that the spatial form, so clear before,
is now less prominent. Conversely, we can turn our hand
toward the sun. The shaded parts, which now face us, become darker as the contrasting gleam on certain parts of the
hand becomes brighter. There is nothing more to be seen of
the finely differentiated pigmentary color that was present

before. In clear sunlight, but especially when something at a distance partially obscures the sun, so that we are standing half in shadow, one can detect mother-of-pearl colors gleaming on the skin. Their magenta and green tones glide over the skin like a delicate veil. In its texture the skin no longer reveals its own details, but rather a pattern that has arisen in conjunction with the rest of the visible surroundings.

The differences we have described will be more or less noticeable, but each picture that arises in this way first gains its real significance in the context of transformation. By imagining pictorially the transition from one phenomenon to another, it becomes possible to anticipate the direction which the transformation will take. Now we are in a position to direct the movements of our hand so that some particular aspect comes to purer manifestation.

The Laws of Nature and the Archetypal Phenomena

The contextual relationships we have described among the visible phenomena, are the expression of a lawful order woven into the fabric of nature. Through thinking we become acquainted with the laws underlying the changing phenomena. But in so doing we do not immediately apprehend nature as an organic whole. Rather, nature is revealed to us at first through particular, characteristic relationships, which singly can be regarded as natural laws.[10]

In physics the starting point has generally been the urge to explain conceptually grasped relationships through processes which, though they elude immediate experience, are nonetheless imagined as tangible, spatial occurrences. Goethe, by contrast, attempted to formulate the individual laws of nature in a way that would point directly to the order already inherent in the phenomena. He sought after "archetypal phenomena," which would contain no unobservable factors.[11]

The context of light is responsible for the fact that we see a visible world. What then is the difference between the "physical" explanation of this phenomenon, and the grounding of the same by means of the archetypal phenomenon? How, for example, do we conceptually grasp the illuminated surroundings of a lamp in each case?

The fact that a lamp is able to illuminate the objects around it is ascribed in traditional physics to a radiation, the properties of which cannot be described here in greater detail. This radiation is said to fill the intervening space by spreading out from its source into the surroundings. To explain how the intensity of the light diminishes with distance, one imagines how an expanding beam of light becomes ever less dense the further it travels from its source. If, for instance, one conceives of a number of concentric spheres centered around the source, then the beam would pass through successively more distended surfaces with an ever decreasing density of radiation. And accordingly, the illuminating effect produced by the beam would be weakened.

Let us now approach the same problem from a phenomenological point of view. We must first consider the visible changes of the lamp and the illumination around it. How do these change, for example, when we walk past a streetlamp at night? As we approach the lamp it increases in size, taking up a greater part of our field of vision. At the same time, we step into parts of the street which are more and more brightly illuminated. If there is a row of identical lamps, those nearer to us appear different from those further away, not in the density of their illumination, but in their perspective size. The conditions described here can be brought to bear upon many other phenomena. The essential thought which connects all of them has to do with the following relationship: if the brightness of an illuminated body changes, this is correlated with a transformation of the visible surroundings perceivable from the place of observation.

The relationship expressed here can serve to calculate effects of illumination just as well as the physical model described above. To be sure, by following up the at first hypothetically assumed radiation of the physical model, it is possible to come very far. But in consequence, one is led further and further away from the sense world, for each successive conceptualization calls in turn for the demonstration of a process in space to actually "explain" it.

A description of the facts in the form of the archetypal phenomenon is satisfied to leave the relationship between the elements of experience in its original, conceptual form. The "spreading of the light" becomes an intrinsic part of the phenomenal context, and is reflected in the different degrees of brightness surrounding the light source. The appearance of the visible objects is always a strict mirror of their visible surroundings.

For Goethe the element of inner harmony, of truth, was the foundation upon which natural beauty rested.[12] The clearly defined shape of a tree, with its play of light and shade, is not due solely to the sunlit context of appearances that binds heaven and earth together: it develops over many years to a particular form within the context of a landscape in which specific conditions of life hold sway. Natural beauty exists wherever specific, characteristic expressions of this kind are able to develop in a consistent way. This beauty is supported by the natural lawfulness accessible to thinking. The contextual relationships in the world then constitute a harmony that permeates the sense qualities. A conscious understanding of such mutual relationships, can be cultivated by an approach that does not attempt to explain the experiences of thinking through a process in space that is quasi-objective and yet does not belong to the pictorial experience.

Imaginal Relationships and Geometrical Optics

We do not easily renounce the wish to explain optical phenomena through underlying spatial processes. For indeed they offer us two "advantages": What would otherwise be a purely conceptual relationship can be delegated to an objective process which takes place by itself; and secondly, this explanation points to a material basis.

Space is the element which we can understand geometrically. From their optics lessons, everyone remembers having constructed the paths of light rays with the help of straight lines. The visible phenomena are understood by mentally looking at the event from the side, as it were, and connecting the related parts as though by stretched threads. The question arises, whether in fact there are any phenomena relating to the propagation of light which exhibit such "stretched threads." It can be demonstrated physically that as a result of diffraction, no increasing approximation of a narrow beam to a straight line can be achieved: the smaller the aperture, the further outward the diffraction fringes extend.

Geometrical figures can also, of course, be constructed in the tangible world. We may, for instance, set up a straight row of poles, aligning them through a process of sighting along their tops. In other words, we assess the relative positions of the images and arrange, for example, for the narrow image (of the last pole) to coincide with a predetermined part of the broad image (of the first pole). In such a case we have to do with a process which has been made ever more precise in technology, thanks to human intelligence. The straight line is something we intend, and as such is the means best suited to give criteria, say, for the production of optical instruments that have to be placed into tangible space as precision tools. With geometry we find our connection to the spatial relationships within which our physical bodies exist. Already when discussing the spatial differentiation of the visible world, we discovered the relevance of vision to this level of experience, to the possibility of land surveying with optical instruments. But all this does not yet lead us to our actual inner relation to the visible world.

Living in the Visible World

Just as we are at one with the given world of the senses through our sense organs, so too is our thought organization at one with the etheric world.[13] The condition of our surroundings, their changes—or lack of change—their degree of beauty, though it is felt through the vehicle of truth, is not merely something to be scientifically explained; it constitutes an element within which we unfold our life. A deeper understanding of this will enable us to provide rational criteria for the shaping of our environment.

Out of doors, a *single* sky arches over the landscape. The sun on its path accompanies us, and with it wanders the direction of illumination. Even when the sky is cloudy, the day's light remains *unitary*. The differentiation into nearby clarity and distant haziness always ensues from wherever we are. One can never arrive physically at the place where the shadows visibly take on the bluish tint of the distance.

At any moment of the day, the configuration of light in the landscape is always expressing the "gesture" of the local climatic conditions in interplay with the character of the season. The illumination of the landscape is thus both unified and—in its changeableness—capable of the most manifold forms of expression.

When we enter the darkness of a cave, we leave behind us this weaving organism of light that is spread over the earth. In the light of our lantern the depth dimension comes to expression, leading from the bright foreground into the darkness. From the glow of such a flame, kindled in the dark, is derived the artificial lighting of our houses. This illumination no longer bears the stamp of nature's hourly changing conditions. Let us now leave the cave. The brightness of the daylight gleams on projecting rocks near the entrance and penetrates dimly some distance into the cave. We can move toward this light and finally step out into the open air. We now experience the changed qualities of the advanced hour, and the correspondingly different nuance of the weather. The coldness or warmth of the air, the songs of the birds and the rustling of the leaves, all accompany the light conditions and their changes. We are once more embedded in the total context of appearances, which we had left behind for a time.

As the evening twilight descends, the order which the daylight had brought about, begins to dissolve. Artificial lighting serves, quite simply, to emancipate human activities from the context of nature. We therefore assign a practical task to it: for example, to provide sufficient light for us to carry on with our work. This has a clear objective, namely, to render nearby objects visible. Under certain circumstances our requirements may go beyond mere brightness. For example, the way pigmentary colors look depends on the spectral distribution of the light source, and a suitable direction of illumination can serve to emphasize spatial forms. The lighting should and can be suited to the objects we are working with.

These rules, however, apply only to limited areas within the differentiated totality of an actual illuminated space.

This totality is, moreover, the element wherein we live and into which our thought organization spreads itself.

Practical measures are aimed at achieving particular effects, and yet inevitably they change the whole configuration. The blinding light of a naked bulb can be eliminated by the application of a lampshade, which hides the bulb from view leaving only the bright area on the ceiling (indirect lighting). The spatial forms of the light are then much less definite. One might say, it creates a different mood. But clearly, for the aesthetic value of the arrangement, the essential thing is how in the one case the truth of the relationship reveals itself to our thinking, and how in the other it begins to elude our thinking.

Similarly, one can consider the effect of frosted glass in lighting technology. When used in the place of clear, transparent windows, it eliminates a part of the total phenomenal context which before was given simply by looking out the window into the open. A lighting effect, of course, remains. Something similar takes place when in artificial lighting the actual lighting apparatus is hidden from view. There is no truth in the evenly glowing panel which covers it. The definite shaping of the lit space around a standing lamp with an open shade is usually regarded as a pleasing, "cosy" effect. In this case, a clear contextual relationship is retained among the perceptible bright areas, and this relationship implicitly includes the electric bulb.

In studying the whole history of lighting technology, [14] one discovers how it has only recently become possible to light interior spaces on a large scale, and at the same time in an arbitrary manner. Originally, a fire was lit at ground level. The characteristic picture of faces lit from beneath directly calls up the association of the campfire. De la Tour repeatedly painted the whole configuration of light and shade around a candle. On festive occasions many candles were lighted in a chandelier; these now spread their light from above downwards. The fire on the floor, the candle on the table, or at eye-level on the wall, the chandelier in the ballroom: all give a characteristic type of illumination in which the source of light and the objects illuminated are included in a single phenomenal context.

The electric light gives quite different possibilities. In a lecture room the general hall-lighting may be augmented by hidden spotlights directed at the speaker, who is then lifted out of the general context of his surroundings by the brilliance of the light in which he is standing. He seems to glow with a light of his own. At the same time, the lecturer may possibly be somewhat blinded by the spotlights, which only he can see, so that for him the audience is only a mass of shadowy forms in a dark abyss. In this way, lighting can unintentionally become a dividing element.

Electric lighting can also be raised up to and into the ceiling. Now we see a bright spot overhead which immediately borders on darkness. The surroundings of the light no longer lead our eye to its source; in the total picture, the lamp is isolated. Our thinking cannot make the connection. Bright and dark no longer point to the unitary context of appearances which we experience in the sunlight.

★

These rather aphoristic remarks about the relation of our thought organization to the totality of our surroundings, may serve to indicate the new applications that can result from a deeper attentiveness to the etheric context of phenomena. Toward this end it will be necessary to develop a new classification of the types of lighting. We may take as an example in this respect, the way Goethe's explanation of the reddening of the setting sun was extended by Rudolf Steiner to embrace the total picture of the surroundings.[15]

For Goethe it was an archetypal phenomenon to have the disc of the sun appear red when seen through obscuring layers of atmospheric haze. A full description of the process, however, must include the way the total picture changes: The shadows ascend, and spread especially over the deeper parts of the landscape; we look out of the darkness toward the red of the sunset. This phenomenon cannot be confined to the direction of the setting sun. It only becomes complete when it is related to the overall context of changes during the course of the day.

The contextual relationships considered here from an aesthetic point of view prove themselves capable of bearing specific formative impulses. Precisely such impulses must be sought for by a science of the organic that endeavors to trace the movements of organic development. In fact, the working of the etheric cannot meaningfully be sought outside such a specific context, apart from an organic whole. That is what distinguishes our treatment of this aspect of the world from the purely physical approach, where thinking and experiment alike are shaped by the principles of abstraction and isolation.

Notes

References to untranslated works of Rudolf Steiner are given by GA number (GA = Gesamtausgabe = Collected Edition, published by Rudolf Steiner Verlag, Dornach, Switzerland).

1. *Editor's note:* The reader may find this usage of the word "picture" somewhat unusual. Rather than meaning a physical painting or photograph, it is used here to refer to the *two-dimensional quality* that the visually perceived world has before the depth dimension is inferred through perspective. This non-spatial, non-substantial quality is also sometimes indicated with the words "image" or "appearances," and with the adjectives "pictorial," "phenomenal" or "imaginal."

2. Rudolf Steiner's writings on the theory of knowledge may serve as a guide in discriminating between percepts and what is added to these through thinking. See: *The Philosophy of Freedom* (1894). Spring Valley, N.Y.: Anthroposophic Press 1964; and also *A Theory of Knowledge Implicit in Goethe's World Conception* (1886). Spring Valley, N.Y.: Anthroposophic Press 1968.

3. Rudolf Steiner too pointed to the activity of the light ether, also in connection with world evolution. See: *An Outline of Occult Science* (1910). Spring Valley, N.Y.: Anthroposophic Press 1972, as well as further descriptions in his lectures.

4. Homer, *The Odyssey*, 6th Song, 42.

5. George Berkeley also points to the particular quality of visual as opposed to tangible objects in his essay "A New Theory of Vision."

6. See for instance, Maier, G. "Ein verformbarer Hohl-Wölb-Spiegel." *Elemente der Naturwissenschaft*, 22(1975):33-43.

7. Rosch, S. "Farbe bei Edelsteinen." *Bild der Wissenschaft* 12(1975, no. 11): 66ff.

8. Goethe included an historical survey in his Color Theory, which concludes with a "Confession of the Author." Here he describes how he became involved with the study of light and color.

9. Maier, G. "Mondphasen im irdischen Erscheinen." *Elemente der Naturwissenschaft* 15(1971):12-20.

10. "Nothing is beautiful in nature that is not motivated as truth by natural law. But in order for a natural truth to appear truly in pictorial form, it must be justified by letting all those natural influences appear which have a part in its formation. I discover well-formed stones along a stream, the exposed parts of which are picturesquely covered with green moss. It is not the dampness of the water alone, which has caused this moss-formation, but perhaps a northern slope or the shade of the trees and shrubs, which has influenced the formation in this part of the stream. . . ." Conversations with Goethe, by J.P. Eckermann. The quotation is taken from Eckermann's extensive report on Goethe's advice to the painter Friedrich Preller (June 5, 1828).

11. Goethe's concept of the archetypal phenomenon is developed by Rudolf Steiner in *Goethe the Scientist* (1883-97). Spring Valley, N.Y.: Anthroposophic Press 1950 (chapters X and XV); and also in *A Theory of Knowledge Implicit in Goethe's World Conception* (1886). Spring Valley, N.Y.: Anthroposophic Press 1968 (chapters XV and XVI). See also the methodological indications in the first lecture (Dec. 23, 1919) of his *First Scientific Course (Light Course)*. Forest Row, E. Sussex 1977.

12. A contemporary of Goethe's expressed it thus: "What contributes among other things to make the sight of a beautiful landscape so exceedingly delightful is the perfect *truth and consistency* of nature. . . . From this excellence of

the sight of beautiful nature, is the harmonious and thoroughly satisfying character of its impression to be explained, and also the favourable effect which it has upon our whole thought. . . .'' Arthur Schopenhauer, *The World as Will and Idea*, vol. 3. London: Routledge 1883. Chapter 33.

13. Concerning the thinking organization of man, see Rudolf Steiner, *Anthroposophical Leading Thoughts* (1924–25). London: Rudolf Steiner Press 1973. Article of March 15, 1925. See also the essay by Christof Lindenau in this book (p.199ff.).

14. O'Dea, W. T. *The Social History of Lighting*. London 1958.

15. See the lecture by Rudolf Steiner on Feb. 21, 1923 in *Vom Leben des Menschen und des Erde*. GA 349, 2nd ed. 1980.

Streaming: A Picture of the Etheric
Ernst-August Müller and Dietrich Rapp

"Since nature is the source of movement and change, and since we are investigating nature, we may not remain ignorant of what movement is; for if we lack this knowledge, we will also remain ignorant of what nature is." Aristotle[1]

"There is indeed no other way of proceeding, than to look within man for the essence of what meets us as the outer manifestations of that essence." Rudolf Steiner[2]

Movement

Whatever *has* become, had first *to* become; whatever exists had first to develop. All the while, the antecedents, out of which the existent came, fall into decay. Thus, behind the world of graven forms there lies a realm of constructive and destructive processes, a realm of movement which accompanies the becoming and dying away. These movements flow creatively around the existent things, surrounding them with a sphere of "formative movements." Out of this sphere things experience their becoming and dying away. "Only when we really perceive the dying and birth of every phenomenon, do we see the world's true face."[3]

At that moment in human evolution when consciousness awoke to the sharp outlines of earthly objects, philosophical thinking was first enkindled in man and he began to speculate about these spatial outlines and their origins. "The beginning and origin of existent things is the Apeiron (the boundless undetermined). What the becoming of existent things issues from, however, into that they must also die; for they pay one another fair punishment and penance for

91

their transgression, according to the rule of time."[4] This famous saying of Anaximander of Milos stands at the beginning of Greek philosophy; it inaugurates Western thought. Becoming and dying constitute the sphere into which the things have been placed. Becoming and dying ceaselessly shift the relationship of the things to their origin, to their essence. With the movements of becoming and dying, the origin flows into what becomes and dies and illuminates it from within.

Where movement reigns, there the boundaries of things are effaced. The changing of forms effaces the boundaries of the fixed forms and reveals a "higher organism" for which space is too confining: this organism must live in time. Thus, the transformations of a triangle show the potency of its concept, while the metamorphoses of a plant reveal the fullness of its type. In its movement, that which is moved acquires depth. With its parabolic trajectory, the thrown stone defines the depths of earthly space. The metamorphoses of the plant display the sunlit space, into which it forms itself. The flights and leaps of the animal fill space to the periphery. The actions of human beings penetrate universal space. With movement, all the boundaries of space become permeable. Movements shed light, which shows the origin of things. Movements bring knowledge, because they permit and also map out the processes of knowing.

Movements are not objects in space. There is no object called "movement." And yet, movement is everywhere, permeating and sustaining everything; without it, no things would be, because their coming into being would be precluded. If we obtain the content for our mental pictures from already formed objects alone, then movement remains incomprehensible to us, and therefore unobserved. Yet we believe we see movement; we have an immediate experience of it, before we embalm it in an exact definition (which in-

deed only means something to those who already know movement is without the definition). For example, the flight of a
bird, or the flow of a brook, is seen as a continuum. To us
the movement appears *given*. But let us look more closely!
Epistemologically speaking, what is yielded by pure observation? Not the movement as a process, for this latter, the
continuing condition of flowing interconnection, transcends
the undifferentiated "chaos" of the pure sense data. Nor
can it be that which moves, for underlying this is a conceptual determination (e.g. "bird" or "brook"). Nor can we
speak simply of a vague "something" which is moving; this
"something" is a general, abstract concept by means of
which the "something" is seen to retain its identity
throughout the changes.

Thus, what can be directly perceived of the bird flight
with our senses is, roughly: a patch of color (bird) set in a
surface of another color (the sky). The color distribution
varies from moment to moment. These differences, and
their connection, are discovered through the comparisons
made by thinking. It is thinking, therefore, that produces
the continuum, the fusion of the different flight positions
displayed by the flying bird. Observing changed conditions
is not the same as observing the movement of change itself.
It is the movement of thinking that links the given sense
percepts together as phases of one process. Our thinking is
the actual agent of movement. The experience of the movement of our own thinking, makes it seem as though movement is perceived through the senses. Thus, we "see"
movement because, by means of a half-conscious inner activity, we bring the mental picture of movement to meet the
sense percepts. Only as the movement of our own organism
is movement itself a sense percept.

Hence, our relationship to movement is not merely
receptive; it is *productive*. "Movement" cannot be separated

from cognition, from movements of thought. It can only be objectified formally, in definitions in which cognition freezes its own movements into concepts. Inwardly, thinking remains united with movement. Thinking, "the unobserved element in our ordinary mental life."[5] comes to our attention in the phenomenon of movement. This is the basis for the curious uncertainty which befalls the observer of streaming. Streaming does not allow itself to be distinguished from the observing consciousness as an object. It can be grasped mechanically only with the help of "sections" or "snapshots," whereby the streaming at one moment is subdivided and the parts thought of as momentarily rigid. With these parts, mechanical equations can be set up (e.g. the conception of the force equilibrium on an imaginary cube of fluid).

The flow of a river, undissected and in continuous motion, cannot be grasped mechanically because it cannot be separated from the cognitional activity of the observer. Cognition is stirred from within when it deals with streaming. Implicitly, it is seeing its own activity, into which the movement flows, or better said, out of which it issues. The *archetypal phenomenon of movement lies in the phenomenon of the activity of thinking.* In the following we will try to become aware of the activity which thinking manifests when streaming is followed with comprehension.

The River

The diversity of movement in natural streaming ranges from the bubbling of springs to the dispersion of rivers in the sea, from the cascading of mountain streams to the gentle tow of broad rivers. The *restlessness* of the origin and the *restfulness* of the terminus work together to set the stream in motion. The one releases the movement from solidity, frees it from the rocks to which the liquid clings, and arouses its bubbling origin. The other receives the overflowing spring and hems it in with wet banks, wherein it collects itself and issues forth as a coherent stream, moistening one place after another. Thus, streaming develops between the poles of restlessness and restfulness, between unrest and rest. It springs from the former, it sinks back in the latter. It finds itself in welling forth, it loses itself to the environment in sinking away. The rhythm of systole and diastole pulses through it as it courses from place to place. Everywhere the river is always both source and sink at once; one raises it from the ground, the other bears it down onto the riverbed. The river travels over the ground, and moistens it at the same time.

Even in its streaming, the river is *source* and *sink* at once. The source produces the river's mobility, which allows it to flow freely in all directions; the sink moors the river to its coherent flow—each local movement passes over and into the adjacent movement and seeps away as it were. The river's streaming presents itself to thinking as the polarity of mobility and coherence, mobility and continuity. Each movement which diverges in a particular direction is absorbed and replaced where it ebbed away by a comprehensive movement from the surroundings. Without this continuity, the streaming would be disrupted. In this respect, streaming appears as a self-contained movement. Its typical motion is circling, turning about itself—vortical. Later, in the section on the vortex, we shall see how the vortex reconciles the rest/unrest relationship in streaming and thereby manifests the archetypal gesture of streaming.

Thus, seen abstractly, the immediate phenomenon of streaming is divisible at every point into the poles of rest and unrest, just as the river stretches between source and sea and with these acquires the polar conditions of its earthly existence. (Rest and unrest are the abstractions for streaming in the same sense that space and time are the abstractions for velocity.[6]) The river's meanders reveal a rhythmic balancing of source and sea, which between them bring about the river's flow.[7] The slope of the land between source and sea breaks open the swirling, vortex-forming movement of the stream into meanders in which the river's circling back on itself is not achieved, at least on earth. In its course from place to place the river breathes between bubbling unrest, which swings it out into loops, and sheltering rest, which draws it back into its seaward flow and prevents its encircling itself. Along the slope of the land, the meander rhythmically separates the polarity of rest and unrest. The organism of the river does not traverse this polarity only in the direction from source to sea (in which direction the river would soon exhaust itself), but also in the opposite direction. A reversed river flows through the atmosphere. The winds transport its water in clouds from the sea to the land. The water evaporates from the sea and rains onto the mountains, where it collects itself in springs. A haze of vapor hangs over the sea, a shower of rain sprinkles the springs. The rising vapor spreads over the calm of the sea, the falling rain nourishes the restlessness of the springs. The vapor "enhances" the sea, the rain the springs. Each has a distinct relation to the sun; the vapor colors the sun through turbity, the rain colors it through reflecting it in the rainbow. In the cloud-filled counter-stream which moves through the illuminated heights of the atmosphere, the visible river is itself enhanced; it erects there its own living breathing arch.

On the other hand, beneath the river course there also runs a subterranean "stream." While the seawater evaporates and supplies the springs with pure (sweet) water, the salt increases in the sea. The water of the river percolates down through the riverbed to become ground water. It saturates itself with the salts of the earth. The sea "flows" underground as a "salt stream"[8] via the ground water back into the land.

Stretching horizontally from source to sea, and vertically from unrest to rest, the earthly river is not complete without the two counter-streams, the airborne and the subterranean; together these form a self-contained "river organism."

Thinking can feel at home in this phenomenal totality. In experiencing the complete river organism, the stream of thinking unites with the cognition of streaming, which is itself grounded in thinking; thinking thereby attains the experience of its own context-creating cognitive activity. Thinking consciously integrates its activities (not only its conceptual results) into the phenomena of the world in such a way that it perceives these as *its* phenomena. Looked at in this way, streaming phenomena seem carried by movements which shape them, by activities which constitute them (not merely by conceptual classifications which regulate them). The totality of such constitutive formative movements, insofar as they are beheld by a thinking which experiences itself, may be called the *etheric* world.

In the following section, the attempt will be made to sketch in detail, from the viewpoint of thinking which experiences itself, how streaming unfolds between rest and unrest. The study of streaming reveals itself there as a training in grasping the etheric world. Then in the section *Thinking and Streaming* this viewpoint will itself be developed. The two sections, *Streaming* and *Thinking and Streaming*, illuminate and support each other reciprocally, and must be read with this in mind.

Streaming

Imagine a river. The pole of unrest maintains the motion of the streaming, the pole of rest is present in the river's bed and banks. (This polarity is expressed hydrodynamically in the Reynolds number, that is, in the relation of the density of the flow which impels the stream (unrest) to the friction which holds it back (rest).)

1. *Flowing*

An initial observation is the simple fact that the streaming moves relative to the bank. The river flows past the observer, its drift marked by a floating object. Conversely, if the observer is in a boat, the riverbank moves past him. At this level, rest and unrest remain external to one another. The movement can only be grasped *relative* to some arbitrary point of reference. One discovers that the arbitrariness of the reference point makes the movement relative—the movement "floats away."

Thus, the streaming not only flows away in the usual, outward sense, it also flows away within itself; a double draining away of movement befalls the streaming. Flowing becomes evident in relation to the observer's condition of rest (or movement), but with nothing to mediate between rest and unrest, streaming "runs aground" against their relativity.

The flow flows away. This contradiction, which the simple flowing stream bears within itself, leads us a step further into the nature of streaming and opens the way to a second observation.

2. Gliding

We see that every part of the river is moving. Toward the bank we see a gradual diminution of the current. The movement dies away and melts into the quiet of the bank against which the still water laps. The streaming itself mediates between its own flowing and the bank. This indicates a new, inner degree of freedom of movement. The flowing that passes from place to place is supplemented by gliding—water flowing over and under itself. The streaming internalizes the relativity of the movement: The reference point, the pole of rest for each movement is the movement adjacent to it, past which it flows. Accordingly, gliding is a flowing of movement past movement. Streaming, therefore, is not merely the running aground of something moved against something unmoved (the stationary reference point)—it is itself the mediation between the two. The relativity of movement becomes substance in the gliding quality of streaming; streaming is the reality of this relativity. Streaming's fluid dimension first comes into being through gliding.

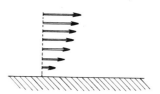

Again at this level of observation, there are two ways in which our thinking could fail to comprehend the actual streaming. On the one hand, the coherence of the streaming could be dissolved through the internal relativity; the streaming could be internally ripped apart. On the other hand, it threatens to stratify, to become differentiated into rigid layers which rub against one another like a shifting pack of cards. The movement of gliding is then pushed *between* these frozen layers, exactly where the fluid is not, and just through this the fluid loses the capacity for gliding streaming. The gliding glides away. The streaming breaks into layers which banish the gliding.

Our observation is pressed further. The gliding cannot be inserted between layers of fluid; it is a quality of streaming *in* the fluid. For streaming is exactly this gliding of the fluid itself, which glides within itself and not as adjacent layers. An additional formative movement of streaming must be responsible for the coherence of the streaming's gliding movement.

3. *Shearing*

Let us think of a compact volume, e.g. a cube, extracted from a streaming medium at any instant. What deformation does this cube undergo as a whole due to the action of the streaming? In gliding streaming, the cube flattens out in the direction of the current. In other words, the streaming volume "shears" open; the angles between its bounding surfaces change. In the diagram, a linear velocity profile shows how the cube becomes a parallelepiped (at least for small regions the velocity profile can always be regarded as linear; for the sake of simplicity, the different components of velocity perpendicular to the plane of the diagram are not considered here). Thus the cube is subject to formative movements that change its shape. These "sculptural" changes occur along the diagonal planes of the shearing parallelepiped (the planes appear as dotted lines in the two-dimensional diagram). The parallelepiped is stretched in the downstream directed plane (a) and compressed (initially) or stretched (subsequently) in the plane directed against the current (b). In this fashion the cube progressively flattens; the stream's voluminal (three-dimensional) quality is overcome through shearing—internally the stream tends to become planar.

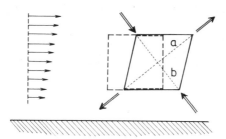

It must be noted that the particular orientation of the diagonal planes (a,b) depends on the shape of the chosen volume. For instance, the more this shape stretches in the direction of the current, the more nearly are its diagonal planes aligned with the current. Because of this element of arbitrariness, we must conceive every shearing stream as filled with innumerable planes along which the shearing sculpts the streaming volume.

Now among these diagonal planes there are, at every intant and at every place in the stream, two special planes that are perpendicular to one another [and are oriented ±45° from the direction of the flow *Ed.*]. These "principal planes" are characterized by the fact that in them, the sculpting stream does *not* shear, but simply stretches or compresses. [The two principal planes are the planes of maximum compression and maximum stretching (tension). *Ed.*] These non-shearing principal planes contain the form-processes of the shearing stream *independently* of the shape of the chosen volume. They thus characterize the shear out of the streaming itself, i.e. not arbitrarily. At every point of the stream, their cross forms the non-shearing skeleton of the shearing sculpture, the *framework of coherence* that permeates and structures the shearing processes of the stream. In this respect these inner form-processes of the sculpting stream relate to the matrix of principal planes immanent in the streaming; these processes establish the stream's coherence, not with volume or material, but with planes, with surfaces. Along these surfaces the stream overcomes its volume and "opens itself up"; between these surfaces the shearing formative movements breathe, stretching and compressing. In this way streaming achieves an open receptiveness, which receives the multidirectional mobility of gliding and imparts coherence to it. The mutual penetrability of movements in streaming is made possible through shearing. The shearing stream is "*coherently open*" for these interpenetrating movements.

The confluence of two rivers provides an illustration of this immanent sculpture that shapes the "open coherence" hidden in the shearing currents. Where two rivers with differently colored water join each other, startling form-processes can be observed along their interface. The interface leading from the peninsula separating the two rivers begins to undulate back and forth, swinging first to one side then to the other. Through this, the coherence of the two rivers is brought about sculpturally. The surface of the river's interface thus increases, until finally the rivers are united. They melt into a single stream which dissolves the original surface of separation.

With the development of open coherence, the stream presents us with a third contradiction. On the one hand, the arbitrary form given the defined volume breaks up the coherence of streaming; under this external assault, the coherence disintegrates into innumerable diagonal planes. On the other hand, the streaming becomes rigidified in the principal planes, thus losing the actual shearing. The full coherence of streaming is still not achieved at this third level; the polarity of rest and unrest within which streaming moves is still not fully harmonized. Therefore the polarity in the expression "open coherence" also seems still to need an adequate resolution. A fourth formative movement is needed to bridge this contradiction.

4. *Turning*

The principal planes, in which streaming radiates its sculptural matrix to every part of the stream, seem themselves to be embedded in a single movement (the fourth formative movement). This movement sums up the movements of all the diagonal planes of all possible small volumes: At each place we observe them, these diagonal planes rotate around a central axis perpendicular to the direction of flow (see diagram). They *turn*, aligning themselves with the current. In so doing, they can pass for a moment through the special principal planes in which streaming, unburdened as it were by shearing, can radiate forth its matrix.

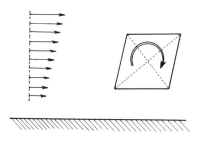

These diagonal planes exist within the continuum of this turning motion, which encompasses them all, yet each turns with a different instantaneous angular velocity, depending on its starting position. This last remnant of arbitrariness, however, is removed when all the diagonal planes in one place are considered together and integrated. A rotational movement is then revealed, determined solely by the streaming, in which the totality of all the diagonal planes turns through the point in the center of the observed place. (An object placed in a streaming fluid rotates with this average angular velocity, for through its own rigidity it integrates all the movements which affect it. A special case is seen in the so-called potential current, in which this angular velocity is zero.) Mathematically, this uniform rotation immanent in the current, in whose unity the individual rotations cancel each other out, is described by the so-called vortex vector. It denotes the "vorticity," the amount of turning of the current at the place in question. The axis around which the bundle of planes turns is called the vortex line.

The mutual induction, by virtue of which each vortex line stands under the motive influence of all the others, causes all the vortex lines to be woven into a whole, whose inner coherence they themselves produce. This dense "vortex fabric" of the stream creates a self-supporting, intercommunicating totality. This network of interweaving vortices is the true *coherence of the streaming*. It permeates the stream in an energetic way, in that it activates the stream's movement from within. Thus the stream appears to be teeming with fine, invisible vortices, which fill it with inner vivacity. They are the "atoms" of streaming movement, the elementary structures, whose inductive coherence constitutes the movement-substance of the stream. They bear the stream's vivacity.

This vivacity is made visible, for example, in the so-called Kármán vortex trains, which have a particularly symmetrical form. They arise as the active response of the stream to the disturbance generated by an obstacle such as a stick or a cylinder (see Illus. 1). The foreign, non-flowing intrusion causes the stream to respond with its own form-processes. It does this by making a rhythmic sequence of alternating vortices, which swing away to either side of the cylinder. In the axes of rotation of these vortices, their vortex lines become visible; in the vortex train, they unite into a lively streaming totality. The vortex train symbolizes the coherence of movement (the inner vivacity) that is characteristic of streaming.

In the selfless, actively streaming medium, the vortex train appears as a multiple echo of the cylinder. The form of the cylinder is reproduced dynamically in the streaming fluid, just as a resting liquid reproduces statically the form of its container and the horizontal surface of the earth. In this way, streaming expresses its actual fluid character—its "creative renunciation" ["*schöpferische Resignation*"][9] with respect to the surroundings, which determine its form. " 'Water' is Maya, and it would not exist in the world were it not spiritually grounded in renunciation, the capacity to refrain. . . . We may say that water can flow in the world, only as it is based on renunciation."[9] The hidden vorticity streams creatively in active renunciation; by virtue of this, the stream develops in itself the particular movement-configuration that its surroundings impart to it. Streaming gives over ("turns" over) its inner vortex-permeated medium to the sides of its channel, and receives these as the sheath (the mold) within which it can manifest. It clothes itself with the fabric of the vortex lines, by weaving the form of the firm sides of its channel into its interweaving vortices. The movement of turning is the process of incorporating the given forms of the channel into the inner sculpture of the currents. The entire stream bears in itself an image of the form of the channel. The streaming arises completely out of itself, and yet is only a reflection of the shape of what bounds it. Thus, the river adapts to the meander, just as it contributes to its formation. The wave running ashore conforms to the mud ripples, even as these have arisen from the wave. In turning, streaming finds the gesture of its self-manifesting activity, the warmth of being directly present on earth.

Streaming's creative surrender to its channel appears to bridge the gap between movement and boundary, unrest and rest, which was our starting point in this section. Streaming itself fills the gap with its energetic vorticity. This vorticity, this moved/moving fluidum permeates the streaming fluid as a higher substance, as the energetic "fluid" that impregnates it and gives it its coherent streaming movement. What really streams, therefore, is not any fluid; it is this *substance of movement* itself which alone is capable of streaming. It is the "movement-ground" on which the streaming treads. The stream does not consist of "streaming" particles (which leaves streaming itself to be explained), but of the invisible vortices out of whose vivacity its movement arises. Streaming makes its way on the basis of these flowing, flexible articulations.

★

This completes the circle of observation. The vortex-permeated medium of movement flows with the streaming in such a way that it is itself the flow, in that it brings forth the flow from itself. On the first level of observation (1) the movement of flowing is visible merely as the movement of a marker *relative* to a fixed point of reference; now it reveals itself in the vortex substance, which arises in accordance with the stream's channel and accompanies the turning movement that unites both the marker and the reference point. In turning (4), the flowing (1) past the bank shows itself to be produced and impelled from sources within itself. The sources of the stream flow along with it: streaming is an *absolute motion*.

With this, the four-level survey of streaming motion proves to be complete; there is no fifth level—with the fourth we are led back to the first. The four-part path fully covers the phenomenon of streaming. Only now does flowing (1) appear in its full light. The analysis which reveals the movements of streaming does not fix the streaming; it leads in the end to a form of thought which immerses itself creatively back into the reality of the streaming, and there uncovers its beginning. The analysis reveals itself as synthesis. The analysis of the simple flowing movement (1), brings to it its origin (4). The path of analysis not only distinguishes a complex of four structures, but eventually resolves itself into an *evolution of streaming* through four stages, each contributing its own formative movement: The turning movement (4) forms the movement-substance of invisibly weaving vortices, which originally endow the stream's coherence with its supple *vivacity*. The shearing movement (3) irradiates this movement-substance with sculptural surfaces, by means of which it opens itself up. Into this *openness*, the gliding movement (2) flows in and fills it with *mobility*, which finally flows away with the flowing movement (1) embedded in the banks. Since with each successive stage the sphere of movement of the streaming becomes related more closely to the physical world, it appears one dimension richer each time (the sphere of movement actualizes itself in, and as, the transition to the physical world): Turning defines the one dimension of the vortex line; shearing opens up the two dimensions of the principal planes; finally, gliding develops the three-dimensonal space where movements freely pass through one another in all directions. When this sphere of movement enters the earth's space, it breaks up and its original movements flow away as rivers, in accordance with the three external dimensions of space. Thus, the movement of flowing anchors all motion to the banks and bed of the river. The external relativity of this

movement is the outcome of this anchoring, which has paralyzed the inner impulse of the sphere of movement. Only in
thinking is this sphere preserved.

Nevertheless, the earth is still "watery" enough to
reveal to living observation a phenomenon which contains
in itself all four formative movements of streaming: the
vortex. The next section is devoted to examining the four-
stage formation and dissolution of the vortex and also its
fourfold behavior.

The Vortex

Let us consider first how a vortex *arises*. Where a river
flows into the sea, there the current detaches itself from the
edge of the shore—through flowing (1) it increasingly frees
itself from the influence of the edge. A surface of separation
thus arises between the moving and the stationary water;
the flow of the river can slip (2) past the (relatively) stationary sea and can glide into it. A gradually thickening boundary layer thus develops, within which the transition from
movement to rest is mediated. Within this layer, consisting
of both sea and river water, the current shears (3) strongly,
that is, the fluid volumes it contains become intensely
planar. The boundary layer then begins to undulate (as in
Illus. 2, where a jet is emerging from a pipe into still water).
Rest and movement here insinuate themselves into one another. This process intensifies until the boundary layer
overlaps itself, i.e. turns back on itself (4), and finally rolls
itself up into a vortex: a vortex has been formed which
rotates around an axis.[10] The previously existent boundary
between rest and movement has gradually, in the course of
the development of the vortex, transformed itself into the
interior of the vortex, forming its core. In this astonishing
manner, the surface of separation is annulled. Instead of

$Re = 36.5$

$Re = 140.5$

Illus. 1. Karman vortex trains formed by fluid flowing past a cylinder (after Homann[24]). (Re = Reynolds number = product of flow velocity and cylinder diameter, divided by the kinematic viscosity of the fluid medium.) The streaming is made visible with scattered aluminum powder, the cylinder extends above the surface of the fluid.

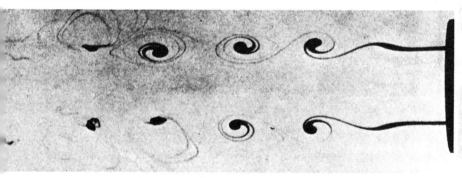

Illus. 2. Jet issuing from a cicrular orifice with a Reynolds number of 1780 (after E. Berger[25]). The boundary layer (made visible with dye released from two points on opposite sides of the opening) rolls up to become a series of vortex rings that encircle the jet; the rings disintegrate downstream.

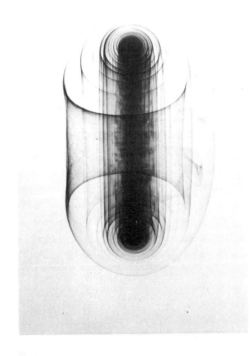

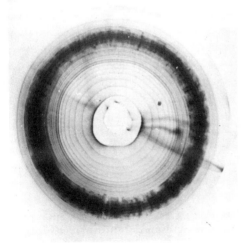

$x/d_o = 3.0$ $x/d_o = 10.0$

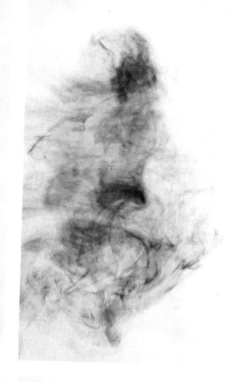
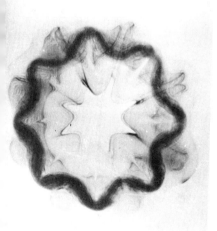

$x/d_O = 11.5$ $\qquad$ $x/d_O = 16.5$

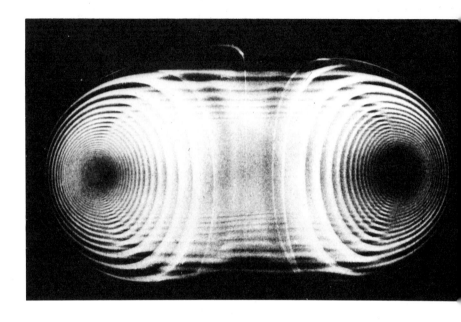

Illus. 4. Well-developed vortex ring (side view) formed after the expulsion of a small volume of smoke out of a circular orifice into air. In the picture the smoke ring as a whole is moving from below upward; at the same time the smoke is wrapping itself around the circular axis of the ring (clockwise on the right side of the picture, counter-clockwise on the left). (After R. H. Magarvey and C.S. MacLatchy.[26])

Illus. 3 (pp. 110, 111). Four stages of a vortex ring formed after the expulsion of a small volume of water into still water out of the circular orifice of a horizontal pipe (dye introduced at the mouth of the pipe). Above: vortex ring seen from the side as it moves from left to right. Below: seen head on. The proportion x/d_0 is the coordinate along the extended axis of the pipe ($x = 0$ at the mouth of the pipe) divided by the diameter of the orifice of the pipe ($d_0 = 5$cm); the velocity of the vortex ring is approximately 7cm/sec. (After C. Leiss and N. Didden.[27])

such a boundary, separating movement and rest, the vortex now mediates between both; its rotation reveals this mediating activity, which was previously hidden in the boundary layer. In the vortex, through the fourfold process of flowing, gliding, shearing and turning, the current has freed itself from the firmness of the shore. In the vortices, identifiable "individualities" have arisen, which show the greatest extent to which streaming is capable of differentiating itself into independent entities.

The vortex axis is the sign of this independence. Since the rotational movement comes to rest in it, it is the bearer of the movement. In it, and in its immediate vicinity, the fluid has the greatest tendency to break up and rarefy; it is the region of maximum suction and minimum pressure. In fluid vortices, this is visible in the gas bubbles which arise or collect there. It is also the region where the most warmth is generated. At the same time, in the region of the axis, the stream has the strongest tendency to cohere, for this region tends to retain what liquid is already there. In the vortex axis, therefore, matter is both bound and released. Only in the immediate region of the axis is there to be seen the increase in angular velocity which is characteristic of rotating solid bodies. Through most of the vortex this velocity diminishes toward the periphery; this is reminiscent of the movements of the planets around the sun, rather than of the rotation of a solid body.

The *behavior* of such a vortex, once this "individuality" has arisen, also shows vividly the four formative movements of streaming. Although the formative movement of turning is not visible near the borders of the stream, it manifests fully in the whirling circulation (4) at the vortex axis. The vortex lines which gather in the vortex are revealed in the axis of the vortex.

The vortex gives itself its own cross-sectional form; as it

wraps around itself it shears (3) over the rim that it (as core) itself brought forth. In repeated cycles around the core, the circulating streaming shears open its own volume into planes. Illus. 4 shows an advanced stage of this process: a vortex ring [which has a circular axis and moves perpendicular to this *Ed.*] is made visible in a smoke-filled atmosphere. Here we can see that the vortex also forms itself as a whole. The shearing processes affect the whole vortex in such a way that they attune the region of the axis and its surroundings (the core and its sheaths) to whatever size and form the vortex is. The turning movement which is more predominant at the axis than shearing, recedes in favor of the latter as the distance from the axis increases. In the axial region of the vortex, the fluid coheres (becomes "voluminal") and at the same time loosens its structure (see above), while at the periphery of the vortex, the fluid "flattens" itself and maintains its consistency.

The vortex actualizes the formative movement of gliding inasmuch as it slides (2) effortlessly (without being pushed) through the surrounding medium, scarcely disturbing it. The smoke rings blown by smokers are a particularly good example of this.

In the vortex ring, each section of the vortex induces a velocity in every other section, each of which in turn induces a velocity in the rest, so that as a whole the vortex moves along self-propelled. Only its rotation round its own axis allows the vortex to move relative to the surrounding medium: it flows (1) entirely out of itself.

Thus the vortex simultaneously binds matter to itself (inwardly) and flattens it (outwardly), it rarefies matter (inwardly) while maintaining its density (outwardly). The vortex is impelled only by itself, and yet is connected with its environment. It establishes a locally independent motion and at the same time blends this with the totality of the stream. It swims through water like a fish, and endows the water with movement. Its most powerful expression is the tornado.

The "biography" of a vortex includes not only its birth and maintenance, but also its *dissolution*. As soon as a vortex ring forms, and thereby loosens its connection with the firm boundaries of the orifice from which it emerged, it begins to dissolve: its "umbilical cord" is cut (1). Once in existence, it "glidingly" draws the surroundings into itself (2), thereby becoming larger, and moves ever more slowly. Thereafter, the vortex axis begins to undulate (see Illus. 3, p. 110 right, and p. 111 left) and the vortex as a whole exhibits characteristic symmetrical forms (3). Through mutual induction, the undulations turn themselves out of the plane of the ring (4) and become pointed. Soon afterwards the ring dissolves in turbulance (see p. 111 right); the inner mobility of the medium extinguishes the previous formative movements and the medium is open to receive new ones.

★

Thus, in its birth, behavior and dissolution, the vortex reveals the fourfold nature of streaming. Its typical properties are manifestations of the four formative movements that are the essential constituents of streaming. The vortex therefore appears as the *archetypal phenomenon of streaming*. Of course, it is archetypal only insofar as thinking is able to see in it the unity of the four formative movements, and to see in these the producers of movement in general. Such insight is based on observing thinking itself. In the following, final section, the attempt will be made to uncover how the foundation of the archetypal phenomenon lies in thinking which experiences itself.

Thinking and Streaming

In the previous sections, in our study of the constituent movements of streaming, we have tried to admit and confirm the creative relation of thinking to movement. Thinking streams into the phenomenon of movement and becomes one with it. It is itself revealed in the formative movements which constitute the reality of streaming. Thinking is that factor in reality in which the activity which builds up reality, itself becomes manifest. In thinking, we can behold the creative formative movements themselves. These movements, which underlie the finished forms of the physical world, appear as phenomena of thinking. It is the nature of thinking to turn "become" into "becoming," to add to the created world the creative gestures. When thinking observes itself (and it would not be thinking without some degree of such self-observation), it appears as the archetypal phenomenon of movement.

However, this archetypal phenomenon is not immediately given to consciousness; it remains hidden to our usual form of thought in which only the perceptible or logical aspects of phenomena are grasped. It is not enough merely to establish that thinking too shows movement, inasmuch as it flows from one concept to the next. For after all, lots of things besides thinking show movement. Moreover, the sea of thinking in which the concepts swim has itself yet to be clarified. It is not the movement *between* thoughts, but the movement of thinking itself that is in question. Even the surfacing and sinking of thoughts in consciousness, their connection and dissolution in the mind, and the mind's deliberate focussing on a concept or a mental picture, are all phenomena external to thinking itself. To uncover the archetypal phenomenon of movement, we need to discover a way to thinking's own movement nature. The close relationship of streaming and thinking suggests it may also be fruitful here to follow the path of the four formative movements which we have traced in streaming.

1. *Flowing*

Let us consider the first formative movement, flowing. Our thinking apprehends this as a condition of a fluid moving through space. Thinking establishes the notion of velocity, which it applies to that which is moving relative to a point of reference (e.g. the observer). The movement is seen as belonging to that which moves. It appears to be its objective condition. This (quite justified) appearance derives from the fact that the *mental picture* of movement enters consciousness without our being aware of how it arose. Whenever thinking concerns itself with something moving, there arises the finished mental picture of movement; it vanishes when thinking turns to something else. The movement does not appear constructed by thinking and is therefore referred to the observed object. In the same way, mental pictures flow past in the stream of consciousness; as stationary observers we watch them from the edge and become aware of their contents. In these pictures the objects of reality appear subjective, that is, they appear dependent upon the observer.[11] They are seen from the perspective of the observing subject, so that their appearance in consciousness is relativized, each person bringing a different point of view. (We all know how the contents of mental pictures can change with our location and point of view. For the engineer of a hydroelectric power station, the mental picture of a river has a quite different import than it does for a fisherman.) This relativity of the mental picture is the product of the linkage of a concept and a sense percept. If the formative movements of the concept are not observed, that is to say, if the thinker remains unaware of them, then the inherently mobile concept becomes paralyzed and absorbed by the sense percept and forced into the perspective in which the percept stands. In the fixed mental picture the mobility of the concept "dries up" and becomes relative; in this condition the concept is captured by the "mathematical" (spatial) and "qualitative" (physiological) contingency of the perceptual world.[12] The danger is that this relativity will become relativism, and thereby preclude all cognitive certainty. The objects to be known flow away with the contingency of the spatial position and physiological organization of the subject. The mental pictures, which are actually supposed to represent reality, disappear from consciousness of their own accord, just as they arose there; they dissolve into kaleidoscopic impressions which simply mirror the different situations of the subject.

2. *Gliding*

Our mental activity does not consist exclusively in watching the stream of mental pictures from the banks of consciousness. We do not only observe the waves on the surface of this stream. We sense that we move with it ourselves, that we impel the stream ourselves, through our mental activity. For we experience that the passing mental pictures, and the standpoint from which we observe them, are linked in our consciousness. Both are mediated by our mental activity. We experience a delicate sense of participating in the stream of mental pictures. The observation is brought forth by us, and to the degree we are aware of this, we as observers are touched by the observation. In this contact, activity and phenomenon begin to gently resonate. The activity of mental picturing begins to enter consciousness—it becomes a mental picture itself, not of course like that of a sense perceptible object, in which the generating activity is lost, but a *mobile* mental picture, in which the activity appears as movement. Here the mental picturing activity meets itself; what it brings to manifestation is itself, inasmuch as it glides consciously over its own movement. In accompanying its own contents, it accompanies itself. It thereby dissolves the link with the sense percept. A mobile mental activity can now flow among all the possible perspectives. Thinking glides across the phenomena without getting caught on them. It remains sovereign with respect to the phenomena because it unearths in them its own movement that generates and develops them. (This kind of thinking is employed particularly in the study of metamorphosis. The gliding transformations of the plant appear in the context of the archetypal plant's mobility in thinking. Similarly, streaming appears in the context of "archetypal water's" mobility in thinking. The emergence and dissolution of a vortex can be seen as a metamorphosis of the different types of streaming that take place in this vivacious archetypal water: detaching, sliding, undulating, involuting as it emerges—disconnecting, absorbing, oscillating, becoming pointed as it dissolves.)

For developing mobile thinking, Rudolf Steiner gives the triangle exercise: "Take a triangle as a starting point, and then allow each side to turn with a different speed and in a different direction."[13] In this exercise, the multidirectional mobility of gliding streaming becomes an event for thinking! We participate inwardly in the streaming in that the mobile picturing feels its own movement and thereby accompanies the picturing. The multidirectionality of gliding streaming is made possible by the fact that each movement is accompanied by another; this becomes a phenomenon in its own right in the mobile mental picture.

Yet, in experiencing its own movement, thinking is in danger of losing its content. It threatens to flow past the relevant interconnections, to glide free of the quiet contours of the given ideal content. The content it loses thereby, again falls out of the stream of thinking and dries up.

Thinking is challenged to enter more deeply into its own nature. "Make for yourself moments of inner quiet, and learn during these moments to distinguish the significant from the insignificant."[14]

3. *Shearing*

Thinking experiences the boundaries of its own movement when it comes in contact with the realities of the world. In this experience, the order of the world begins to guide the movements of thinking. In their free unfolding (not in their final lamed condition) these movements encounter a delicate necessity, which works on them sculpturally. In this boundary experience, thinking does not meet boundaries on which it would be shattered, or past which it could not go—thinking meets the boundaries of a sculpture inherent in its own movements. "The soul learns that these boundaries simply signify the experience of being touched by the spiritual world. Becoming aware of such boundaries is an experience comparable to tactile experience in the sense world."[15] Thinking's gliding movement over the ground of the senses, breaks open upon these boundaries; thinking becomes aware of these boundaries as special mental pictures, as "boundary representations" ["*Grenzvorstellungen*"]. "By their very nature, these representations do not allow themselves to be lamed" and resist being related to any sense reality.[15] The boundary representations, therefore, cannot be pictured after the manner of the things of the sense world. They comprise the inner experiences a soul can have at its cognitive boundaries when it is independent of the impressions of the senses. The boundary representations carry in themselves the essence of the mental picture; they carry what mental pictures are "apart from their sense-world content," namely, "a force within the soul available for the development of spiritual organs."[15] In the boundary representations "the first opening of the soul to the spiritual world" occurs.[15] They constitute the sense-free experience of the boundaries, and are themselves these boundaries—they are organs of touch, and are the active power of opening. The essence of the mental picture meets itself in these boundaries—they eliminate the laming and deadening influence of the sense percept and they open the soul for pictures in which the spiritual contents of the world can appear.

The boundary representations bring to the (developing) soul the power to open itself, just as shearing brings this power to streaming. In shearing the stream sculpts itself according to the principal planes, thereby opening itself up to the moved and moving surroundings. The principal planes dam up the streaming movements, thereby pressing them into each other to form an "open coherence." In the matrix of the principal planes, streaming experiences the law of its flow, the environmental integration of its own coherence. The sculptural movements of shearing do not appear in a given stream in which a rigid channel cripples the movement. Every form stamped on a particular stream by its channel, is the expression of the sculpture of the streaming deadened by the influence of the channel. The inner sculptural nature of the stream appears in the principal planes, whose open matrix repels the laming impressions of the channel. (This comes to expression, for instance, where two rivers converge—though admittedly in many instances the sculpture inherent in the streaming remains an "open secret.") As our mind's picturing activity finds the power to open itself in the boundary representations, so does a stream find the power to sculpturally open itself in the principal planes.

The streaming, however, cannot manifest its watery nature—which is to receive the formations of the surroundings into itself—if it remains enclosed within its own sculpture, upon which its own coherence depends. Similarly, the picturing activity cannot remain in the region of the boundary representations, where—as the content of the world presses in on it—it still touches only itself and knows the impressions of the world only through its own variations, through its own skin as it were. However sublime, this picturing would remain merely a reflection of external contents, were it not capable of shedding this sensitive skin and, with a final turn, creatively grasping the contents themselves; that is to say, it must uncover in itself the lawfulness of its own creations. One who wishes to develop his cognitive powers, must get beyond "looking only at himself."[14] At the same time, "everything reminiscent of external impressions must be set aside. The quiet inner contemplation, the converse with the pure spiritual world must fill his whole soul. . . . He must learn to love what streams to him from the spirit."[14]

4. *Turning*

Just as the principal planes prove to be embedded in a turning, rotating movement, so the boundary representations reveal themselves to be alive and inwardly active to those who develop a "living feeling for the silent activity of thinking."[14] And just as in turning, the inner sculpture of the stream follows the shapes of the channel and reproduces them, so also do these living representations fill themselves with the formations of reality. "The picture bites into reality."[16] Such representations, which the soul apprehends as alive, are also termed by Rudolf Steiner "*Imaginative representations.*"[15,17] "When one has reached such inner experiences as those found in the realm of pure thinking, experiences which reveal themselves as the experience of freedom, one then attains to a metamorphosis of cognition with respect to the inner world of consciousness. . . . One now enters into the realm of pictorial, Imaginative thinking. One attains to Imaginations that are real, that are no longer merely inside oneself; through them one is placed in an objective world."[18] In the Imaginative representation the mental pictures are saturated with reality—they display a sequence of pictures of reality. This turn-around, this involution of the boundary representation into the Imaginative representation, is made possible through surrendering our picturing activity to the world in such a way that the world content unfolds within it. "Thus the process of cognition becomes fitted into the order of universal reality. In cognizing, man participates in the creation of this universal reality."[19]

This turning of thinking, through which thinking proves itself to be a formative movement of reality, unfolds picture-creating substance in thinking; in this substance, the reality-saturated essence of thinking can manifest. "In Imaginations, in mental pictures, in representations that have a fuller and more definite content than abstract thoughts, one finds what one needs to comprehend the human being as a conscious being. One must resolve [*man muss die Resignation haben*] not to go on further, . . . not to let sense-free thinking simply roll on through its inner inertia . . . , one must resolve to stay put and confront within oneself the 'outer world' of the spirit."[18] Thinking that brings itself to manifestation at the borders of its activity, where in full activity it suspends its own processes, such thinking is pure will, the creative ground of the contents of the world which it thinks. The point where thinking holds back [*resigniert*] with respect to its own movements, and reflects them inward, proves to be the fountainhead of its origin. This renunciation at the boundary of the world is creative—it brings the wellspring of the world within itself. It opens up the "wellsprings of the world in which the experiences of the soul bubble forth out of true reality."[20] This "creative renunciation,"[9] which flows in Imaginative pictures, is the movement-substance of thinking and of reality. With this renunciation thinking opens itself creatively to reality—it gives up merely copying what it previously regarded as reality. "Through having accustomed oneself to the kind of thinking that emerges in the course of *The Philosophy of Freedom* ('pure thinking, in which the ego can live and maintain itself'[17]), one becomes capable of such acute inner exertion that, while one is perceiving with the senses, one can exclude or suppress the mental pictures and devote oneself entirely to perceiving"[21]; in this way one sucks in the percepts "without modifying them all the while with mental pictures."[21] "We particularly train ourselves to be filled with the content of perception . . . when instead of grasping these contents in pure thought, in lawfully logical thoughts, we henceforth grasp them in symbols or pictures, and thus allow the content of perception to circumvent the thoughts as it streams into us."[17] Through "surrendering oneself to the outer world"—above which the ego hovers in pure thinking—"we attain to knowledge of the spirit; and when we raise to consciousness what we otherwise do unconsciously in perceiving, we perceive how the spirit enters us through the senses and organizes us."[21]

This organizing activity links us to the outer world without making us dependent on it. It is the form in which the spirituality of the outer world is present within man's creative renunciation; it is the activity of the places where thinking's boundary representations transform themselves into Imaginative representations about the world. It is *the etheric body of the human being*.[18] The "etheric water" of his creative renunciation streams into the formative processes of mental representation. This water is the medium (the true "unobserved element in our ordinary mental life"[5]) that flows in Imaginations and is transparent to reality. It forms the substance of thinking in the same sense that the vortex-permeated movement forms the substance of streaming. As the former consists of Imaginative representations, so does the latter consist of invisible vortices, whose ability to become visible "images" is shown when streaming reproduces within itself the forms of its channel or when in free streaming these forms become actual vortices. Just as pure (sense-free) thinking apprehends the (spiritual) outer world in Imaginations, so does free streaming "image" in vortices the formations of the sides of the channel it has freed itself from. This vortex-permeated "form" of the streaming, whereby it stands in active connection with itself and with its surroundings, may be regarded as the "etheric body" of the stream. It adapts the internal coherence of the stream to the surroundings. It flows formatively with and within the stream, without flowing away. The invisible vortices are the turning, flowing organs of the stream's etheric body.

We are drawn to try to find in the turning movement-form of the vortex, an Imaginative representation of the etheric nature of streaming. Through the four-part study of streaming and its constitutive movement-substance (symbolized in the vortex), it is possible for meditative thinking that experiences itself in its Imaginative roots, to arrive at a true picture of the etheric. "Thinking belongs to the events of the world, it draws you and your soul into itself; you live in these events when through thinking you let the essence of thinking flow into yourself."[22]

★

Let us recapitulate. The formative movements (introduced in the section *Streaming*) that constitute every stream and bring it into motion, are the concepts with which thinking co-produces the reality of streaming in conjunction with the senses' experience of streaming. Furthermore—and this is the unique aspect of a study of streaming—the senses' experience of streaming can be accompanied by thinking's experience of movement. Hence, in the realm of thought processes, the concept and percept of streaming flow together and thereby become experienced as gestures, as formative movements that contain the genesis of streaming. Thus enlarged by its own genesis, streaming appears in a higher light.

The method employed here does not involve erecting hypothesis about non-experiencable factors behind the appearances, or through formalisms coercing the phenomena into functional interpretations. Instead, the phenomena are brought together to form a self-supporting totality, which emerges of itself and in so doing explains the phenomena archetypally, out of themselves. In short, the principle of experience in science is made complete through the inclusion of the experiences of thinking. The light that illuminates and orders the appearances, now appears itself. This "higher experience within experience"[23]—as a constituent factor of reality—also belongs to the totality of observed reality. It uncovers the etheric dimension of reality as the *genesis* of reality. Thus, a more radical application of the principle of experience, leads of itself to a spiritual science of nature. There is no reason to apply the principle of experience only to the world of the senses. The capacity of thinking to observe itself breaks down the dogma that all valid experience must be sense experience. Thinking, which has always been presupposed in interpreting sense experience, now itself becomes experience; thereby the principle of experience is fully plumbed and science has achieved its presuppositionless basis. Since self-experiencing thinking brings with it knowledge of the reality of the etheric formative movements, the etheric proves to be that entity in which the *presuppositionlessness* of reality becomes substance. The etheric is the medium of evolution; in this medium reality reveals itself out of its own creative sources. The foundation of reality is not some kind of quasi-sensuous "thing in itself," but rather the only *experiencable* substance that is capable of generating reality in a manner that can be experienced: it is living thinking itself, in which the "wellsprings of the world"[20] are active, in short, etheric substance.

A science of the etheric nature of streaming comprises exactly these formative movements of reality in which thinking and streaming flow into one another (as the parallel structure of the sections *Streaming* and *Thinking and Streaming* attempts to show.) In the formative movements of streaming, self-experiencing thinking finds the pictures of its own activity—an activity in which the etheric of the world is streaming. To say this, is not merely to make a vague analogy between the streaming of a river and the streaming activity of the etheric; in a strict sense—insofar as living thinking productively illuminates the reality of streaming's formative movements—streaming is a real (not allegorical) *picture of the etheric*. In this picture, thinking perceives its own etheric activity; in the fourfold buildup of streaming, thinking develops its own living nature (from ordinary (1) to Imaginative representation (4)). By unfolding the reality of streaming in four stages, thinking differentiates the picture of the etheric and characterizes the different kinds of etheric activity.

A science of streaming built up meditatively in the fashion attempted here, incorporating the description of the experience of thinking, brings with it a path of training. On this path thinking develops itself for spiritual science and at the end can produce that presuppositionless concurrence of

knowing and happening (thinking and streaming) which is
contributed to reality by the etheric:

"I feel myself, thinking,
   At one
   With the stream of world happening."[22]

Notes

References to untranslated works of Rudolf Steiner are given by GA number (GA
= Gesamtausgabe = Collected Edition, published by Rudolf Steiner Verlag, Dornach, Switzerland).

1. Aristotle. *Physics*. Bk. 3, Chap. 1.

2. Steiner, R. *Warmth Course* (1920). Spring Valley, N.Y.: Mercury Press 1980.

3. Steiner, R. *Geisteswissenschaftliche Behandlung sozialer und pädagogischer
   Fragen* (1919). GA 192, 1964. Lecture of September 28, 1919.

4. *Die Fragmente der Vorsokratiker*, edited by Hermann Diels, Hamburg 1975.

5. Steiner, R. *The Philosophy of Freedom* (1894). Spring Valley, N.Y.: Anthroposophic Press 1964. Chapter 3.

6. Steiner, R. *First Scientific Lecture Course (Light Course)* (1919). Forest Row,
   E. Sussex 1977.

7. Schneider, Peter. "Ab-Fluss oder Ab-Wasser, ein Innenwelt- oder Umwelt-
   problem?" *Elemente der Naturwissenschaft* 19(1973):29–36.

8. Steiner, R. *Natur und Mensch in geisteswissenschaftlicher Betrachtung* (1924).
   GA 352, 2nd ed. 1967. Lecture of February 9, 1924.

9. Steiner, R. *The Inner Realities of Evolution* (1911). London 1953. Lecture of
   November 14, 1911.

10. *Editor's note:* Depending on the conditions, the axis of this vortex may form a
    complete ring around the incoming stream. When the surface of the water in-
    terrupts the ring, the axis is represented by the familiar cone-shaped depres-
    sion of the water surface.

11. See note 5. Chapter 6.

12. See note 5. Chapter 4.

13. Steiner, R. *Human and Cosmic Thought* (1914). London: Rudolf Steiner Press
    1967. Lecture of January 20, 1914.

14. Steiner, R. *Knowledge of the Higher Worlds and Its Attainment* (1904) 3rd ed.
    Spring Valley, N.Y.: Anthroposophic Press 1947. Chapter 1.

15. Steiner, R. *The Case for Anthroposophy* (1917). London: Rudolf Steiner Press
    1970. Chapter 1.

16. Steiner, R. *The Younger Generation* (1922). Spring Valley, N.Y.: Anthropo-
    sophic Press 1984. Lecture of October 5, 1922.

17. Steiner, R. *The Boundaries of Natural Science* (1920). Spring Valley, N.Y.:
    Anthroposophic Press 1983. Lecture of October 2, 1920 (evening).

18. See note 17. Lecture of September 30, 1920.

19. Steiner, R. *A Theory of Knowledge Implicit in Goethe's World Conception* (1886). Spring Valley, N.Y.: Anthroposophic Press 1968. Footnote to page 2.

20. Steiner, R. *The Riddles of Philosophy* (1914). Spring Valley, N.Y.: Anthroposophic Press 1973. Last chapter.

21. See note 17. Lecture of October 3, 1920.

22. Steiner, R. *The Threshold of the Spiritual World* (1913) (published together with and listed under *A Road to Self-Knowledge*). London: Rudolf Steiner Press 1975. Chapter 1.

23. See note 19. Title of chapter 8.

24. Homann, F. "Einfluss grosser Zähigkeit bei Strömungen um Zylinder." *Forschung auf dem Gebiet des Ingenieurwesens* 7 (1936), 1.

25. Berger, F. *Uebergang von laminar zu turbulenter Strömung.* Wiss. Film C 816/1960. Inst. für wiss. Film, Gottingen, 1960.

26. Magarvey, R.H. and C.S. MacLatchy. "The formation and structure of vortex rings." *Canad. Journ. Phys.* 42(1964).

27. Leiss, C. and N. Didden, photos from: Das Max-Planck-Institut heute (E.A. Müller) *Z. Flugwiss.* 23(1975):168–173.

The Formative Movements of Plants[1]
Jochen Bockemühl

As described in the essay on the elements and the ethers
(p. 1ff.), the mode of observation belonging to the watery
element is also appropriate to the growing green plant.
Goethe practiced this mode above all in his study of plant
metamorphosis. Rudolf Steiner worked out the epistemo-
logical basis for this and sketched the essential features of a
new science of the organic realm in his book *A Theory of
Knowledge Implicit in Goethe's World Conception.*[2] In this
book one is led to see that it is not enough to describe the
plant—using more or less static concepts—as a spatiotempo-
ral structure; the plant must be grasped as an entity in per-
petual transformation. If one lives into the "streaming" of
the plant, into its transformations and metamorphoses, one
soon becomes aware from within of a danger which from the
outside is often focussed on exclusively. The danger of
swimming in formlessness with the idea of metamorphosis
was also recognized by Goethe.[3]

The word "swimming" can mean losing oneself in gen-
eralities, and this is indeed a danger. But one can also *learn*
to swim, that is, to move with purpose within the watery
streaming element, to proceed in a certain direction and
cover a certain distance. In this case our clear thinking consciousness can guide us. This consciousness was engendered
through meeting up with the realm of objects, but now the
task is to free it from these objects so that it can become a
guide. This is achieved by bringing to consciousness the *activity of ideation* itself. As a preparatory exercise, we may
practice mentally transforming one triangle into another

through gradually changing the angles or the lengths of the sides. The different leaf forms of a plant can in principle be derived from one another in similar fashion. In the exercise with the triangles the *direction* of the mental movement is determined by us; with the plant the direction is characteristic of the plant itself. *Mentally*, we can derive the first leaf of the plant from the last or the last from the first, but in the plant the direction of the sequence of forms is fixed. With the plant it is particularly important to grasp the direction along with the mental movement that brings the individual forms into motion.

When in our observation we progress from one organ of the plant to the next, trying to follow the transformations with our thinking, we find ourselves dealing with a movement that of course does not really take place in the outer sense world; each leaf has arisen separately from the plant and has not developed through a physical transformation of the previous leaf. The movement grasped by our thinking therefore represents an ideal relationship between the separate phenomena, and together with them comprises a particular aspect of reality. Goethe tried to characterize this movement with the concepts "expansion-contraction" and "progressive metamorphosis."[4]

Taking as an example the Common Sow Thistle (Fig. 1), we can see how development begins with smaller, simpler forms, progresses to more complicated ones, and then near the flower passes back again to simpler forms. What is happening in this process can become clearer if one pays attention to the *direction*.

Expansion and contraction characterize at first quite generally, a movement which originates from, and then returns to an ideal "zero point." A movement of this kind can be symbolized by a curve such as a loop or a lemniscate. These curves pass through a single point twice, but the direction is different each time. This aspect of such curves suggests a new arrangement of the leaves in Figure 1. When the individual leaves are arranged in a loop, as in Figure 2, the least expanded and the most contracted leaves both appear near the ideal zero-point. The leaf in which all parts are developed to the same degree—the leaf at the level of greatest manifestation—appears furthest from this point.

What can we observe here? The loop arrangement shows clearly how during the phase of expansion the plant's development tends toward the periphery. The stem of the leaf lengthens and the parts near the top of the leaf become ever more richly differentiated. Then the direction shifts. Already before the middle of the sequence the base of the leaf begins gradually to broaden. The contracting phase which now commences is characterized by a formative tendency that is polar to the tendency during the phase of expansion. Those parts of the leaf close to the axil become ever broader, while the expanse of the distal parts steadily diminishes. This process is accompanied by a shortening of the whole central leaf axis.

Thus the phase of contraction is not simply a reversal of the phase of expansion; if it were, the sequence in Figure 2 would be symmetrical. Within the sequence as a whole an inner shift occurs, which can be read from the changing proportions of the forms.

The individual leaf forms also participate in this "shift of direction." The early convex forms become concave. Rounded forms become points. Thus at the start an almost round leaf blade is carried on a thin stem, while at the end of the movement the stem has disappeared and the broad leaf base is drawn out to a long thin tip. Seen in this way, the individual forms become "signposts" for the plant's movement of development.

Let us see in another example how this arrangement in a

Figure 1. Mature leaves of a Sow Thistle (*Sonchus oleraceus*) arranged in the natural vertical sequence.

134

Figure 2. Complete mature leaf sequence of a Sow Thistle (same as in Fig. 1) arranged in a loop.

135

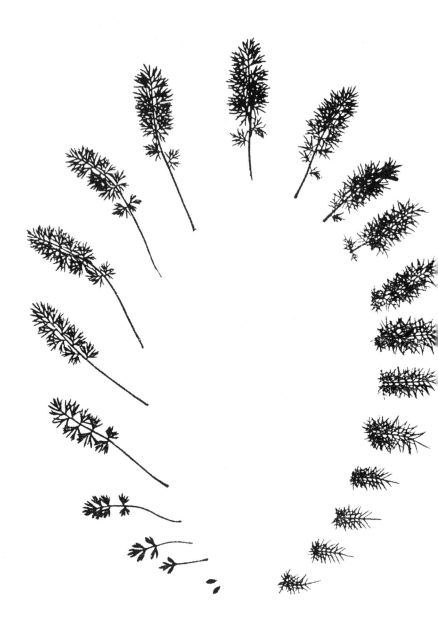

Figure 3. Complete mature leaf sequence of "Love in a Mist" (*Nigella damascena*).

loop can bring out general laws of development. In Figure 3 the loop for a plant from a completely different group is shown (Love in a Mist, *Nigella damascena*). The basic "theme" which runs through this sequence of forms is completely different. There is, for example, a strong tendency from the beginning for the leaf blade to be very finely divided. But if we grasp the outline of the whole leaf, ignoring the fine divisions and the density of the leaflets, we see the same overall formative tendencies as in the Sow Thistle. After the relatively round seed leaf there follow long-stemmed leaves with expanded blades which are ever more finely divided into densely arranged leaflets. The change of direction that now occurs can be clearly followed in the stem as it begins to shorten, thus bringing the leaf base down to the axil. The base of the leaf becomes emphasized by the increasing density of the leaflets, while at the distal end these become thinner and more thread-like.

These examples suffice to show how the metamorphic movement of a plant has the inner quality of a "loop." The very different forms of the two plants nevertheless show the same direction during the course of the movement. In seeing the leaf series as a loop, it becomes easier to visualize the laws of the changing forms.

Seen as the form of a movement, the loop enables us to characterize one aspect of the nature of the plant. It shows that we are seeing part of a larger movement which, as it comes from the previous fruit and seed and extends to the flower, passes through a zero-point and undergoes an "involution."[5] It is significant in this regard that the planets as observed from the earth also move in loops.

The Formative Forces and the Time-Body of the Plant
The "watery" mode of observation[6] leads us to a level where we are dealing with the etheric formative forces—also

in the image of the plant—and where we may be able to experience the plant's etheric body. A further study of the leaf forms will illustrate this in detail.

As we have seen, the complete sequence of mature leaves from an annual plant gives the picture of a self-contained, formative movement. This sequence reflects the plant's whole movement of development in a distinctive way. The development of each individual leaf, however, can also be regarded as a formative movement. Starting with these two aspects allows us to come to a first experience of the formative forces. If we follow how they mutually interpenetrate, we begin to have a glimpse of how the "time organization" works, by virtue of which a living organism is distinguished from a dead one.

1. *The formative movements in the development of individual leaves*

Let us first consider the development of single leaves, in order then to compare their formative movement with that of the sequence of leaves of the whole plant, as already described. Figure 4 shows the development of one of the first leaves of *Cardamine hirsuta*, the Hairy Bittercress. A very small spike first separates out of the growing point. This grows and divides, soon giving rise to five spikes. The leaf blade forms between them. The growth of the green leaf surface takes over the whole periphery. The stem of the leaf separates itself off from the blade. A shoot-like formation bunches up and grows in such a way that the leaf blade is carried outward, away from the main stem. The spikes grow out quickly, but become steadily more rounded—they are, in fact, overtaken by roundness. The blade which at first was spiky is now a uniform rounded shape, and contrasts sharply with what has now become a long leaf stem.

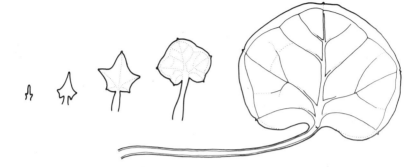

Figure 4. Development of one of the first leaves of Hairy Bittercress (*Cardamine hirsuta*).

The processes of leaf growth can be described in various ways. It is common practice to make a distinction between growth in length, breadth and thickness. Such a description is based, more or less consciously, on relating the Cartesian coordinates to the developing leaf. One can also distinguish the regions of vegetative growth, for example, between the growth of the tips and the intercalary growth. In this discussion, though, the attempt will be made to describe growth in terms of the different formative tendencies which can be distinguished within the total process of development.

When we speak of spikes, stems or blades of leaves, we are referring to specific elements of form. But if we attend to the transformative processes between the different stages of development, these elements of form may be described as formative tendencies, or better, as formative *activities*. We make these activities our own when we transform one form into another in thought.

The first activity of which we become aware we shall call *sprouting*. A spike forms and grows out in a specific direc-

139

tion. Insofar as this multiplies, another activity is added, which we shall call *segmenting*. The activity which gives rise to extended leaf surfaces we shall call *spreading*. Similarly, the activity whereby the region near the base of the leaf lengthens and consolidates to a stem we shall simply call *stemming*.[7]

The process of forming the leaf thus shows itself to be composed of four distinct activities differentiated in space and time. In the course of this discussion, the validity of distinguishing just these four activities will become more apparent.

Both the first leaves and the final leaves have been described by others as "inhibited forms" [*Hemmungsformen*],[8] whereas the leaves in between are regarded as "typical." We can largely agree with this, but we must still ask what kind of "inhibitions" these really are. Do not general laws become manifest precisely through the particular way in which the different organs of the plant are inhibited, and do these laws not help us better understand the dynamics of the plant? Are not the "inhibitions" accompanied by "promotions" in other respects?

If we answer the questions affirmatively, the first and final leaves will appear as special expressions of the type and not merely as incomplete foliage leaves. It would, in that case, be easier to regard the type as a definite but mobile form within a stream of changing shapes, instead of restricting it to a particular shape.

If we observe the formative movements in the way described, and trace the interpenetrating activities, it already becomes clear with the single leaf that some activities begin earlier, others later, and that they also cease at different times. According to the intensity and duration of the various activities, the form of the leaf looks different at each stage.

In *Cardamine hirsuta* (Fig. 4) we have already noticed

how spikes arise at first through sprouting and segmenting. Then, as spreading allows the leaf surface to expand, the sprouting activity dies away. The spikes persist for a while as serrations in the margin, but then disappear almost completely into the blade. This interaction between sprouting and spreading can proceed in many different ways and to a great degree determines the contour of the mature leaf.

Figure 5 shows the development of a basal leaf of *Glechoma hederacea* (Ground Ivy). In order to compare the forms, the scale has been altered, which gives some distortion. For our purposes it is most advantageous to depict each stage of the leaf the same size. The actual size relationships are depicted underneath in black.

The first stage shows several spikes that are still sprouting (the degree of magnification makes them look rounded). Spreading has already begun in the first stage, while sprouting and segmenting begin along the lower leaf margin until the fourth stage and then largely die away. The rounded lobes at the margin in the fourth stage are engulfed by the ever more intense activity of spreading. As though the apex and base of each lobe were held by a knot, the spreading bulges out between them. In the process, parallel veins are left behind, which appear like ripples. The mature leaf form displays indentations exactly where at first there were spikes.

The whole form of the leaf also changes in a characteristic manner. The initial oblong shape differentiates into a broad kidney-shaped blade and a long stem. The mature leaf is almost entirely an expression of spreading and stemming.

2. *The formative movements of mature leaf sequences*

Let us now consider sequences of forms of mature leaves in a similar manner. It should be readily apparent from the examples we have considered that the formative movements of such sequences must give a quite different picture from the formative movement of a single leaf. Troll[9] quotes Wretschko's observations of the leaves of *Umbelliferae*: "The leaves that arise along the main stem to the inflorescence, display to a certain degree the various stages of a development of a single basal leaf." This is also approximately the case in other plants, and thus has naturally prompted the aforementioned thought that the final leaves are inhibited forms of the larger earlier ones. But there are other ways of looking at this phenomenon.

If we look once more at the series of forms that a developing leaf of *Glechoma hederacea* passes through (Fig. 5), we do see more or less the picture of the sequence of mature leaves along the stem, but significantly, the order is reversed. We shall return later to the fact that the formative movements of the single leaf, and of the whole sequence of mature leaves, run counter to each other. Furthermore, we must be clear that the sequence of mature leaves resembles not so much the stages of the individual leaf depicted in black (Fig. 5), but rather the artificially enlarged versions

Figure 5 (pp. 142–143). Development of one of the first leaves of Ground Ivy (*Glechoma hederacea*), each stage enlarged to the same size (actual relative size in silhouette below).

with their modified size relationships. Thus the plant itself as it were, carries out a corresponding "distortion."

The form sequence of *Valerianella locusta* (Corn Salad, Fig. 6), is particularly clear and simple. In the early mature leaves, stem and blade are entirely separate. Two elements of form develop distinctly and then gradually merge into each other. In between, various intermediate stages of interpenetration are evident: step by step the blade pushes toward the base of the leaf. In so doing, the blade elongates and incorporates the stem into itself.

Here too, beginning with the perceived elements of form, we can grasp the process of transformation (which we ourselves complete inwardly) as an interplay of distinct activities. We are less tempted here than with the previous examples, to identify these activities with actual processes of growth. The formative movement unfolds more obviously on an ideal level.

Seen in terms of the activities we have already identified, *Valerianella* is dominated by spreading and stemming. It is a

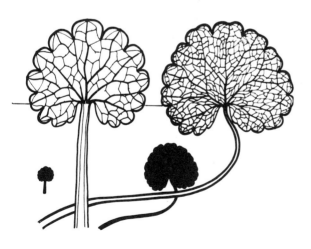

very simple example, in which we can follow the interplay of these two activities particularly well. We notice that they display a certain lawfulness. In speaking of "expansion and contraction," Goethe grasped this lawfulness as a totality. During the phase of expansion, stemming and spreading are largely *separate*, whereas during contraction they are *merged* with one another. This can be taken as a general rule. Even when, in the phase of contraction, part of the stem remains distinct, the blade usually shows a definite tendency to elongate and incorporate the activity of stemming into itself.

The middle region, in which both activities interpenetrate, can look different with each species of plant. There each species distinguishes itself through a particular motif, which is taken up and varied in the formative movement. If we look more carefully at these formative activities of stemming and spreading, we find, as we did when considering the development of individual leaves, that these two alone are insufficient. In the contracting phase the forms hint at segmentation and become slightly pointed. Segmenting and sprouting are obviously also at work here.

In *Cardamine hirsuta* we have already observed how the two activities of sprouting and segmenting can become obscured in the mature leaf. Figure 4, however, shows only the development of one basal leaf. If we consider the forms of later leaves, the picture changes, as we see in Figure 7. At first, stemming and spreading also predominate here. Then the whole form of the leaf begins segmenting into leaflets. It segments very early and so thoroughly that the stemming activity can reach up into the individual segments. One basic component is multiplied. Stemming and spreading interrelate in such a way that the separation is preserved. As if from within, the leaf blade is taken hold of by the activity of stemming. Spreading is confined to the peripheral regions where independent stalked leaflets form. These are at first

Figure 6. Complete mature leaf sequence of Corn Salad (*Valerianella locusta*).

145

round, but then they too segment, becoming elongated and more pointed. After segmenting, sprouting sets in at the end.

The four activities—stemming, spreading, segmenting, sprouting—appear here in a sequence that is the reverse of the one displayed by the developing basal leaf. Here too, in the course of expansion and contraction, they follow definite laws. In *Valerianella*, with respect to the first two activities (stemming and spreading), we have already gotten to know *separating* and *merging* as such laws. As we saw, the two other activities, segmenting and especially sprouting, can remain hidden during the phase of expansion. They are enveloped as it were by spreading. In between the initial expanding and the final contracting phase, these activities can *interpenetrate* in various ways. Thus, for example, in *Cardamine hirsuta* a highly segmented leaf emerges—the segmenting reaches into the realm of the stemming, and the spreading is confined to the outer regions. While stemming and spreading gradually merge during the phase of contraction, thus elongating the unsegmented leaf, the sprouting in the leaf segments brings about a characteristic modification of the contour.

Thus, at the end of this phase of development, elements of form can arise which have a polar relationship to the initial forms. A good example in this respect is the leaf sequence of an annual shoot of *Medicago sativa* (Alfalfa, Fig. 8). Here the tripartite segmentation of the leaf is retained throughout. Only the topmost leaf is simple. All the parts, both main and side leaflets, are at first round and plump, later becoming elongated and more pointed. Most remarkable, though, is the way in which the indentations at the distal ends of the early leaves are later replaced by rounded points. This process is reminiscent of the developing single leaf in *Glechoma* (Fig. 5), where signs of the early segmenta-

Figure 7. Complete mature leaf sequence of Hairy Bittercress (*Cardamine hirsuta*) from seed leaf to flower.

tion are retained in the notches in the margin of the mature leaf, and the pointed lobes lying in between are so overtaken by spreading that indentations appear in the place of points. The notches of the first leaves of *Medicago* correspond to such indentations, and have arisen in the same way. In the phase of contraction, though, sprouting predominates. Again here, we observe formative movements that have opposite directions.

This raises the question how far these four activities are separable. The contrast between sprouting and spreading is clear. The one progresses in a particular direction, the other spreads out in a plane. It is considerably harder to recognize the corresponding contrast of sprouting and stemming. As both bring about elongation, there is a temptation to regard them as *one* activity operating in different regions of the leaf. Nevertheless, in another respect they are fundamentally different from one another. Sprouting is characterized by the growth of points or spikes. Its tendency is to ray out from a center. The tip grows outwards and the leaf is left behind. In contrast, stemming arises through intercalary growth (mainly at the leaf base), which pushes the leaf outward. Its tendency is to form radii and to consolidate these in the stem. Otherwise, when stemming is active in the region of the leaf blade, it forms veins running parallel to the leaf axis. In regard to the total leaf form, the growth arising through the two activities of sprouting and stemming proceeds in opposite directions.

Through making the distinction between sprouting and stemming, it also becomes possible to establish the significant contrast between the first and last foliage leaves as they typically appear in annual dicotyledons. The phase of expansion (which includes the seed leaves) is dominated by stemming and spreading. Sprouting and segmenting are held back. By contrast, during the contraction phase,

Figure 8. Mature leaf sequence of Alfalfa (*Medicago sativa*).

sprouting dominates and stemming is held back. When spreading and segmenting are still evident in this phase, they are confined more and more to the base of the leaf.

The overwintering basal leaves of perennial plants will not be specially considered here. They fit well into the picture if one places them not at the beginning of a new season of growth, but at the end of the previous phase, in which indeed they were formed. As they belong to the phase of contraction, they are naturally related to the upper leaves, only they do not lead to flowering but to a new phase of vegetative growth. If they are stirred to new growth by the next year's expansion, they then characteristically grow, not at the tip of the leaf but at the base, as do all the lower leaves. In this way the loop depicted earlier (p. 135) becomes a closed circle within the vegetative realm. The situation with the seed leaves is often similar to that of the basal leaves.

If one thinks away the fourth activity (segmenting), then the other activities only produce a simple, wholly unsegmented leaf. Conceptually, segmenting stands close to separating (cf. p. 144). However, it leads to a repetition of the same, whereas separating—as a superordinated law—has to do with qualitatively different tendencies (separating relegates stemming and spreading to separate regions).

The more vividly metamorphosis is experienced as movement through our own inner activity, the more clearly we realize how the actual formative movement passes rhythmically between two poles—expansion and contraction, separating and merging, "making an individual space" [*Eigenraumbildung*] and "openness to the surroundings" [*Umweltoffenheit*].[10] At the same time, we begin to notice two distinct perspectives: From the first perspective we experience a differentiation among the forces forming the plant; what is shown here is a path toward experiencing four *formative forces* as they express themselves in the formation of the leaf. From the other perspective we see a plant species' characteristic motif, which determines the interplay of the forces so that an actual *form* can emerge. Without this motif the effect of the forces would be completely dispersed. In the form motif of the leaves of a particular species or group of plants a higher level of experience is already indicated, about which we shall yet come to speak.

3. *The development of individual leaves in relation to their sequence*

We still have the task of following the developmental movements of the individual foliage leaves of a plant in connection with its total development. To begin with we can picture such a combined movement with the help of Figure 9, using the Hedge Mustard (*Sisymbrium officinale*). This figure shows the leaves from four plants which germinated and grew in the same spot *at the same time*, and which were later harvested one after another at intervals of about a month. It shows what has not been apparent hitherto, namely that in each stage of growth the plant produces a picture of both "expansion" and "contraction." With plants 1 and 2, this is immediately evident in the illustration. With plants 3 and 4 one must add in imagination the early leaves, which have in the meantime already wilted and fallen off. To aid our imagination, we can refer to the fully developed leaves of the other two plants (as indicated by the solid black arrows). That the leaves in the sequence become larger and then smaller is not so significant here; rather it is the typical distribution of the long-stemmed, relatively

▶

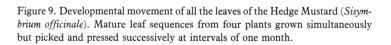

Figure 9. Developmental movement of all the leaves of the Hedge Mustard (*Sisymbrium officinale*). Mature leaf sequences from four plants grown simultaneously but picked and pressed successively at intervals of one month.

3

4

round forms on the left, and the short-stemmed, more pointed forms on the right. In the central region, the largest leaves are also the most highly segmented.

If we follow the path through the four stages that a single leaf would take (indicated by the light arrows), we find the previously discovered counter movement to be strongest in the lower leaves. The light arrow between plants 1 and 2 indicates how a leaf shifts during the development from being within the contracting phase to being within the expanding phase. This counter movement becomes steadily less pronounced with the later leaves. All these observations allow us now to follow and characterize the whole complex of movements in more detail.

4. *The interplay of the formative movements*

The two formative movements are summarized graphically in Figure 10, which shows representative stages in the development of the leaves of Nipplewort (*Lapsana communis*). The mature leaves are arranged in a loop as before. This loop defines the periphery of the diagram, toward which all the other forms are directed. The central zero-point represents the origin of the development of all the leaves. From here radii ray out to the mature leaf forms on the periphery. Between the center and the periphery various representative stages of development are depicted. The radii connect forms in which the four formative activities stand in approximately the same relationship. The (curved) arrows proceeding from the center trace the development of individual leaves. Were plants to grow like crystals, these arrows would correspond to the radii. In general, however, the direction of development of a leaf is constantly shifting.

The first step of development is the same in all leaves; this step points in the direction of the form of the last mature leaf (below right), which stands closest to the flow-

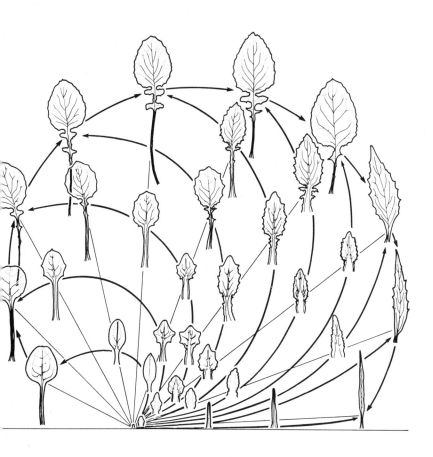

Figure 10. Developmental movement of the leaves of Nipplewort (*Lapsana communis*). Partially schematic representation of the relation between the changes of form during the growth of individual leaves from growing point to mature leaf (arrows radiating counter-clockwise from center), and the changes of form in the sequence of mature leaves from the seed leaf to the highest leaf (outermost arrows clockwise).

er. Only in this leaf is the formative movement of development almost linear. All the other formative movements diverge from the radii more or less strongly. The lower leaves diverge most, thereby cutting across radii that lead from the origin to mature forms that will only appear later (further up the stem). Thus, the developmental stages standing at these crossings are like premonitions of later mature formations.

The outer loop in the diagram is the now familiar sequence of mature leaves up the stem (clockwise arrows). Each form appears there as the meeting place of two movements that run counter to each other. This "movement picture," of course, can only be a weak reflection of the actual processes. The form of the middle leaves is particularly expressive of these processes, but it is after all only one form among many.

Perhaps this survey of the developmental processes in plants can be a key for other processes of development. Could it not help us understand the appearance of so-called "prophetic" forms in the evolutionary record?

Expressions of the Time-Body in the Formative
Movements of Plants

In modern science, much effort has gone into describing the characteristics of the different kingdoms of nature. For our immediate experience, inorganic and organic processes are very significantly different, yet it is a constant challenge for us to grasp the differences satisfactorily.

It is not enough to enumerate various particulars; we need to see how these make a whole. It lies in the nature of a candle flame to hold a stream of movement in balance; this structure may be described as a "flow form." The formative movements of a plant are, by contrast, intrinsically involved in constant transformation, following a higher lawfulness. What manifests in space as a stream of movement in the flame, is "pulled apart" in the plant to a process in time, to a "time-form."

It may be objected that the processes in the flame also

take place in time. These, however, are uniform; they do not change qualitatively from moment to moment, but only alter in response to changes outside the flame itself. Time is, so to speak, external to such a process, whereas in the plant the transformations are not only shaped from without, but are primarily the expression of its own internal time, the structure of which shall occupy us below.

In flowering plants it is known that only up to the point of maximum differentiation—i.e. only within the phase of expansion—do the changes in leaf form proceed as a purely vegetative process. The phase of contraction is already a preparation for the flower (or for a period of dormancy). The forms of the upper leaves can indeed only come into being through growth, through the building-up of substance, but these forms are nevertheless progressively held back by the later to appear flower. The vegetative leaf must go through a kind of zero-point before the flower can appear.[12]

A direct reshaping of the form requires that besides a building-up, also a breaking-down of substance be incorporated into the life process. This is first found in animals. Such breakdown processes underlie the movements of the animal insofar as it is impelled by its inner drives. These movements are the expression of an inner soul realm. Now in the plant the equivalent of such a breakdown process already lies in Goethe's concept of contraction, as it is perceived in the formative movement of the mature leaf sequence. Only this does not manifest substantially here, i.e. it does not appear as a physical reshaping, since each subsequent leaf is formed anew. That which in the animal brings about the change of form and movement from within, works here from without, limiting (inhibiting) the growth of the leaves.

This limiting activity, which co-determines the form, does not, of course, operate only during the phase of contraction, but participates in the forming of every leaf. Flower formation presupposes not only contraction, but the whole vegetative development; the beginning of the "contracting phase" simply indicates the predominance of the limiting activity, and therewith the approaching flower formation. Plants like ferns, which in their formative movement show only expansion, not contraction, also do not form flowers. Their reproduction remains in the vegetative realm, and then in the prothallium stage joins the damp earth. In only a few ferns (e.g. the Ostrich Fern) does the sporophyll contract at all, and these are therefore rightly seen as transitions to the flowering plants.

Already here we perceive that two polar processes underlie the development of plants. We can see this still more clearly by surveying the formative movements of a plant, as we tried to do with the Nipplewort in Figure 10. There we saw how a mature form that is to appear only later can be prefigured in the formative movements of the individual leaves of an earlier stage, and then how this form can again disappear.

Where the inner spiral movement meets the counter movement of the periphery, there stands a mature leaf. Every leaf originates as the product of these two movements. If the path along the outer loop is short, then the path along the spiral is long and strongly curved. A leaf that emerges after the plant has undergone much development— in other words, one that one reaches on the outer loop only after traveling far to the right—passes through only minor changes of form in its development and has a path that is weakly curved, approaching a straight line.

A rough picture of every stage of the plant's development can be obtained from Figure 10 if one links together the developmental stages the different leaves are passing through at a particular moment in time. (Figure 9 is based on four plants and shows four particular stages of development.) Thus one sees that at each stage the plant displays both form tendencies—expansion as well as contraction. In the course of the plant's development this picture only becomes clearer and spread over a greater number of leaves.

What do these processes tell us about the nature of time? In the realm of sense perception, we can only grasp time as a one-way sequence. Every physical process unfolds in this way. The living, developing organism, however, reveals through its formative movements the presence of a counter stream of time; the organism holds the two streams in balance.

What was known by the ancient sages is confirmed here, namely that the nature of time is not exhausted by the sequential appearance of things in space. On another level, which is accessible to us only through inner observation, time flows in the opposite direction.[13] When the picture of a yet to be enacted deed gives direction to our will, we experience the effect of a stream that we constantly allow to enter our lives from the future. The actual deed we enact in the world of the senses, on the other hand, takes place in the opposite direction, in the familiar stream of time that flows from the past to the future.

With the plant, in the sequence of leaf forms, we have a series of unfinished pictures that have prompted us to observe an *ideal* movement underlying the plant's development. The *real* (substantial) transformations of the leaf pass through the tendencies of this ideal movement in the opposite direction. Thereby, from leaf to leaf, the "substantial movement" of the developing leaf is progressively modified. Here, through the "drives" of the plant visible in the picture of the sequence of forms, something is revealed which only on a higher level, in man and animals, appears as a true soul capacity.

To the thoughtful observer, two qualitatively distinct formations will have become evident through the foregoing, one spatial, the other temporal. Where a formation of this sort distinguishes itself from its environment through its own form, so that it appears as a separate entity, we may speak with Rudolf Steiner[14] of a *body*. The form of the body is always determined from a higher level of reality.

Thus, the flow form of the flame exists as a *spatial* body (physical body). Changes arise here only through outer factors; time remains "external." In the plant, through the constantly changing spatial body, we can apprehend the expressions of a *time-body*. These appear pictorially in the formative movements. In spiritual science, this time-body is also called the life body or etheric body.[15] Its elements are the mobile, interpenetrating *etheric formative forces*, which on our path of observation we encountered as "activities." The form of the etheric body derives from the superordinate *astral* realm, which has only been touched on here. In the plant the astral realm is not formed into a body as it is in animals. That is to say, plants do not have an "inwardness" corresponding to their outer form.

Notes

1. This paper brings together material from several earlier publications: Bockemühl, J. "Der Pflanzentypus als Bewegungsgestalt." *Elemente der Naturwissenschaft* 1(1964):3–11.

   — "Bildebewegungen im Laubblattbereich höherer Pflanzen." *Elemente der Naturwissenschaft* 4(1966):7–23.

   — "Aeusserungen des Zeitleibes in den Bildebewegungen der Pflanzen." *Elemente der Naturwissenschaft* 7(1967):25–30.

2. Steiner, Rudolf. *A Theory of Knowledge Implicit in Goethe's World Conception* (1886). Spring Valley, N.Y.: Anthroposophic Press 1968. Chapter on "Organic Nature."

3. Goethe, Johann Wolfgang v. "Problems" (1823) in *Goethe's Botanical Writings*. Honolulu: University of Hawaii 1952.

4. Goethe, J.W.v. *The Metamorphosis of Plants* (1790). Wyoming, R.I.: Bio-Dynamic Literature 1978.

5. Suchantke, Andreas. "Die Metamorphose bei Blutenpflanze und Schmetterling." *Elemente der Naturwissenschaft* 4(1966):1-7.

6. See the essay "Streaming: A Picture of the Etheric" in this book (p. 91ff.).

7. *Translator's note:* The author's terms for these activities are *Spriessen, Gliedern, Spreiten* and *Stielen*. These are most simply rendered as sprouting, segmenting, spreading and stemming. Conventionally, science borrows from Greek or Latin for this purpose, but the author's preference is for an unusual use of the vernacular.

8. Troll, Wilhelm. *Vergleichende Morphologie der höheren Pflanzen* vol. 1, part 2 "Vegetationsorgane." Berlin 1939; Göbel, Karl. *Organographie der Pflanzen* part 1. Jena 1928.

9. See Troll, note 8, p. 962.

10. Schad, Wolfgang. "Zur Biologie der Gestalt der mitteleuropäischen buchenverwandten Bäume." *Elemente der Naturwissenschaft* 7(1967):11-24;

    Göbel, Thomas. "Das Fruchtblatt in der Pflanzenmetamorphose." *Elemente der Naturwissenschaft* 8(1968):44-54.

11. Howald, Mario. "Ganzheitliches Forschen im Anorganischem." *Elemente der Naturwissenschaft* 7(1967):1-6.

12. Bunsow, Robert. "Die Bedeutung des Blühimpulses fur die Metamorphose der Pflanze." *Elemente der Naturwissenschaft* 5(1966):1-10.

13. Compare Steiner, R. *Study of Man* (1919). London: Rudolf Steiner Press 1966. Lecture of August 8, 1919.

14. Steiner, R. *Theosophy* (1904). Spring Valley, N.Y.: Anthroposophic Press 1971. Chapter 1.

15. See the essay "The Concept and Action of the Etheric Body" in this book (p. 217ff.).

Scientific Thinking as an Approach to the Etheric*

Wolfgang Schad

The Modes of Scientific Thinking

That which anthroposophy terms "the etheric" is not perceptible to any bodily sense organ. Rudolf Steiner (1904, 1910) described this realm out of supersensible experience and drew attention to manifold phenomena as evidence of its working within the sensible realm. Perceptions of this kind arising out of earlier states of consciousness, such as, for example, the "ka" of the Egyptians or the "archaeus" of Paracelsus, become comprehensible today in this way, but not *vice versa*: we do not possess the ancient forms of consciousness, and where remnants of this are still present, they must be superseded by present-day consciousness. The consciousness of the present is that of modern natural science. The question is whether this attitude of consciousness bears within itself the capacity to find an empirical approach to the etheric. This question must be raised if the etheric is to be accessible to modern, rigorously self-consistent waking consciousness. This essay will attempt to describe a way in which such an approach might be developed.

As is already clear from the above, such an attempt founders on unscientific nebulousness if it seeks the etheric within the realm of bodily sense perception in the way that, for example, Kirlian photography and other modish "psi-

---

*This contribution is an expanded version of the author's essay "Biologisches Denken" (Biological Thinking)—see Schad 1966.

phenomena'' do (Binder and Kirschner 1975). The safest initial assertion that can be made concerning the etheric is that it cannot take the place of physical energy, for otherwise it would reside within the physical realm, and thus be quantifiable and subject to the law of conservation of energy, into which balance it does not enter.

Yet it is precisely the sense perceptible to which natural science addresses itself. How is it, then, that despite this, science is taken here as an access to the etheric? This question makes it clear that the etheric becomes accessible not through the bodily sense organs, but rather where science proceeds beyond the activity of observation—indeed, where it first becomes a science: in thinking, in scientific thinking.

Rudolf Steiner depicts the etheric as that which brings every living being to life: an autonomous capacity to behave within matter, physical energy, space and time in a way different from that of lifeless objects. Thus our first task must be to conduct an inventory of the modes of thinking that have appeared in the biological sciences. We must therefore make the forms of our biological thinking in its various applications themselves the object of our further investigations. Which modalities of thinking do we find within biology? In earlier times teleological thinking prevailed, a thinking that seeks final causes. Since the second half of the last century, this mode has been swept aside by causal explanation. Later we will speak of a third. What gives each its explanatory value?

Let us first turn to the causal mode of explanation. Today it is customarily held to be the only exact, scientific mode of thought. Its principle is the causal nexus. This principle states that every observed condition is the effect of a temporally prior cause, and, in addition, that every cause or every causal context can have but one kind of effect. All future events are thus necessary consequences of the present causes and these in turn the necessary effects of prior causes. The phenomena are determined in their sequence by the preceding conditions in the causal nexus. In causal explanation, the essential thing is that every phenomenon is recognized to be the product of its past.

The relationships stand differently in the case of teleological explanation. In contemporary scientific circles it is no longer considered an exact mode of explanation. Yet in countless particulars the organization of living beings appears so purposeful that, if one but looks for it, teleological interpretation in terms of purpose and goal still crops up frequently in the teaching of biology. Some kind of agency, explained no further—today "nature" for the most part—is supposed to have organized this or that in accordance with specific purposes. To be sure, such explanations are offered not in full seriousness, but rather with a trace of astonishment, and in quotation marks. Yet even if, for the most part, this is not done in full seriousness, nevertheless in popular presentations today a wealth of questions is still answered in this way only. But what is the essential nature of this mode of thinking? A final purpose lying in the future works back upon the present relationships in such a way that they be come the means by which this final purpose is effected. The means are prior, and their future effect is the purpose. The essential factor here is that the determination works backward from the future. Teleological explanation recognizes a phenomenon only by virtue of its being conditioned by the future.

We come a step closer to the essential quality of each of these modes of explanation when we observe their applications. In which areas of science does one encounter primarily the causal mode, and in which the teleological?

The *causal mode of thinking* we find especially in physics and chemistry. Here this mode has been able to develop itself relatively unhindered, and surely this is connected with the way in which these areas of science, now seamlessly joined, have developed: each has evolved its method through dealing with *inorganic* nature. Here causal thinking has the clear advantage of presenting fewer boundary experiences than would another mode of thinking, because lifeless phenomena obviously can to a great extent be deduced from their past states and understood in this way. There is no better schooling in causal thinking than the study of these scientific disciplines. The determination of physical events is, however, not absolutely valid, for in the microphysical realm of elementary particles, atomic events cannot be predicted exactly in terms of macroscopic, "classical" quantities (e.g. time and energy), but rather only in terms of probabilities. It is, however, essential to macroscopic inorganic events that the statistical mean value of elemental probabilities does not exhibit *variable* regulation. Thus within the macroscopic dimension the causal nexus attains full validity.

Where is it that *teleological modes of thinking* are principally employed? This is the case especially in psychology. Teleological explanation presupposes a quality in the object that is oriented toward the future. This is actually the case in all drives, wishes, desires, longings, hopes or whatever else we call such faculties in everyday speech. Brentano (1911:122) spoke of intentionality, Craig (1918) and Lorenz (1937) of appetites. Spranger (1924:13) has noted that it is not at all necessary for these psychic contents always to have a fully conscious character: often they effect a teleology that remains "unconscious" even to themselves. When hunger emerges as an observable content of the soul, its objective meaning and purpose, namely to maintain the organism, does not at all need to be a content of the subjective consciousness. The desire for nourishment presses toward this goal nevertheless. It is the same with the instincts for flight, reproduction, mothering, etc. The context in which these dull psychic processes have meaning is part of an overreaching, or as Spranger says, "objective" teleology, which it is often entirely unnecessary to resolve first in the subjective consciousness.

With the participation of the constructive consciousness that looks to the future and premeditates, as for example in the case of a technologically creative person, the application of causal methods simultaneously reappears. Such conscious planning is, however, always set into motion by genuine drives, wishes and needs, without which the execution would not occur. Here also the actual future-oriented component is the will. To the extent that it projects into the future, its present bears the stamp of that same anticipated future. The essential quality of the will is that it always relates to the future. All phenomena that bear such a relationship to the future can be explained in teleological terms.

Now it is also clear where causal and teleological thought-constructs are out of place. The parabolic path that has been traced by a stone thrown obliquely can be derived from the initial conditions, and thus in causal terms (the initial acceleration of the throw and continuing acceleration in the field of gravity). The parabolic form does not arise because the stone would like to describe such a curve for any purpose. On the other hand, as Spranger (1924:21) says, Socrates did not sit in prison principally because the metabolism of his leg muscles brought him there. Even knowing that certain psychological characteristics can be influenced by hormones does not help the psychologist in any way to explain them. The chemical substance can function only as the liberator of capacities that must already be present potentially in the

realm of the soul. Both teleological explanations in the inorganic realm of substance and causal explanations in the
psychological realm of the will are out of place.

Our thinking normally enters of its own accord into the
time-relation of the phenomena in question when we think
correctly. The dead world exists as such by virtue of its past
alone. Through the inorganic the world's past persists
within the present. The instinctive-ensouled realm is likewise unable to do much with the present, since it yearns in-
cessantly for a still unreal future. Through the realm of the
soul the anticipated future is harnessed to the present. If
one regards the present as something that has been effected,
then its causal condition lies in the past, while its teleological condition lies in the future.

Now biology is a scientific discipline the objects of
which, to the extent we are interested in them as living organisms, stand between the inanimate realm and the realm of
the soul. Biology touches both realms, in that on the one
hand the organism continually releases dead matter, while
on the other hand the animals—particularly the higher animals—exhibit anticipatory behavior. Thus causal and teleological modes of explanation have been applied to biology in
various ways. As is well known, there has been no lack of attempts to interpret the living organism from either the one
or the other point of view; to reduce complicated processes,
true to the principle of economy of thought, to more simple,
fundamental processes. Those more intimate with the
material aspect of the world used every opportunity to
derive the organism mechanistically. Those closer to the
side of psychological experience sought the fundamental life
processes there—men like Driesch (1908), who spoke of the
"psychoid"; or Strombach (1968), who seeks them in the
unconscious psyche. For Rensch (1968)—as for Haeckel
(1917)—even the atoms of the inanimate world are en-

souled, a totally undifferentiated monism that simply closes its eyes to the multiplicity of realms of experience.

Today we find neo-Darwinism widespread within the schools of biology. Its persuasiveness stems from its attempts to explain in causal terms what has hitherto been conceived teleologically. Automatically, i.e. without any guiding psyche, natural selecton destroys the deleterious mutants from the overproduction of each population, so that those having gained an accidental advantage survive. The greater the pressure of natural selection, the greater the increase in adapted individuals. It became possible to abandon teleological explanations that assumed a purposeful anticipation of the future in favor of abundant factual data generated when the causal—i.e., future-blind—principle of natural selection was hypothesized.

★

If one reviews what the Darwinian approach can and cannot explain today, one sees that it is largely accurate for the development of morphs, aberrations, varieties and races. For the evolution of genera and families, not to mention orders, classes or even phyla, Darwinian research offers only speculative constructs, by which we mean here everything that is not experimentally verifiable. No biologist has ever seen a spruce become a fir or a rose a plum tree, let alone been able to breed them. Between race and genus stands the mediating concept of species. Whether or not natural selection (or isolation as negative selection, as a lack of selection) proves adequate depends upon the breadth of one's conception of the species. That which is possible in the case of species in a narrower sense ("microspecies") cannot be fixed in the case of species in a wider sense ("macrospecies"); not to mention that a unified concept of species is not feasible (Overhage 1965:148-168, Schilder

1952). One thing is certain, namely: that the whole of *trans-specific* evolution (transspecific = "extending beyond species") exhibits no experimental bases for a neo-Darwinistic interpretation. Peters (1972) has described this state of affairs in greater detail, and called for complementary models and constructs. In fact, it can be shown that in the realm of the higher systematic categories the evolutionary stages carry out not an increased adaptation to the environment, but rather an increased *emancipation* (Kipp 1949, Schad 1977:257ff.). In addressing such questions one must realize that every organism present to the senses belongs simultaneously to each and every systematic level. To the extent that it is morph, strain and subspecies, the organism is subject to environmental adaptation in the Darwinian sense; to the extent that it is a member of its genus, family and especially its order and class, it exhibits degrees of freedom and autonomy of basic structure that remain recognizable despite all convergences: otherwise it would not have been possible since Linnaeus to construct a natural systematics in place of his artifical one. Only when viewed in this way does one become aware of the significance of the concept of species as the vitally necessary organizational complex that mediates between the two antinomies. This is already apparent in the most frequent conceptual determination of the species: the sum of all individuals that are able to produce fertile offspring together. In mating, the mate is always the single organism's "environment" on the one hand; yet on the other, in terms of protein biology, it has nearly the same immanent characteristics. Suchantke (1974) has recently clarified this intermediate position of the concept of species in the case of butterflies.

★

Since the suspected purposefulness of adaptive characteristics has often proved to be an illusory teleology, many biologists today seek signs of purposefulness only when considering all the integrated characteristics. If such characteristics are purposeful with regard to the maintenance of life, then they are deemed open to Darwinian interpretation. Countless phenomena are thus interpreted factually through the demonstration of a teleology that is subsequently viewed as illusory, even though in the vast majority of cases the habit of determining the supposed causal nexus experimentally has yet to be acquired. Neo-Darwinism seeks teleologies and then explains them causally. Where it cannot find them, it remains unable to explain in causal terms. The result is a continual short-circuit between the two kinds of conditions, because one is working under an assumption that is eliminated again immediately thereafter. The problem of life is neither causal nor teleological, nor is it a dualistic "both-and."

Much research has been done concerning the connection between body and soul. Most researchers have concluded that this connection does indeed exist, but that it is impossible to grasp it in a clearly demonstrable way, even in terms of brain physiology (Rein and Schneider 1964:602). This assessment is valuable, because it shows that the connection can be resolved neither upon the somatic nor upon the psychological level. Steiner was the first to make clear where it lies: between the psychological and the somatic level lies a realm unto itself, essentially different from the other two, a realm that can be apprehended neither by external sensory observation nor by psychological introspection: it is the *activity of life*. Its autonomy has stood the test of all the "spontaneous generation" experiments and is thus already—in pragmatic scientific terms—among the most quantitatively secure data we have. Humans themselves experience this realm unconsciously, subconsciously. For, psychologically speaking, vital processes always run their course in a state of unconsciousness. And yet the reality of these sleep-processes is indisputable. In keeping with an ancient usage,

Steiner calls them the realm of the etheric. This is a realm that exists neither physically nor in the realm of the soul, but rather effects and constitutes the connection between body and soul because it communicates with both—something that material and psychological processes can never do directly.

Thus in every organism one is concerned not with purely lifeless and purely psychological processes, but first and foremost with processes that are predominantly vital. These have been impossible to derive in terms of causal analysis and remain so. The now widespread descriptions of the guidance of protein synthesis according to the base sequence of nucleic acids (DNA) have usually suppressed, for example, the fact that this is possible *in vitro* only through the removal of the nuclease enzymes that break down the nucleic acids (Matile 1973). These proteinaceous enzymes are built up *in vivo* by the DNA, just as they themselves act to break down DNA. No one-dimensional causal connections prevail here. The teleological mode of thinking remains equally unsatisfying here, because it also misses the unique quality of life. Both modes of explanation fail in the face of actual vitality, no matter how much they contribute to the investigation of the boundary conditions. With this we hit upon the central characteristic of the life-processes: *as such they are determined not so much by previous or future conditions, but rather at each moment by their own present.* The conditioning events are no longer separated in time from their effects; rather, condition and effect coincide temporally to a greater and greater degree and finally become equivalent in their mutual influence. Steiner once termed it a "relationship of reciprocal causality" (1922).

★

Research into ontogenetic life processes has already broadened out in this direction within biological cybernetics. This field seeks to trace the ways in which the one-dimensional causal relationships in the organism are turned back upon the original conditions so that each consequence works retroactively. The causal chain is closed into a regulative *loop*. A step toward comprehending the relative constancy of every internal biological system, the homeostases (Cannon 1932), was made when these came to be viewed as cybernetic phenomena. Linear models were replaced by models with more complex ramifications and—what is essential—by retroactive networks of effects.

What did this accomplish? It accomplished the dismantling of one-dimensional thinking even within the schools of biology. Since then, even the mechanistically oriented biologist now dares to tackle the problem of *wholeness*, the fundamental quality of the organism. Yet in principle biological cybernetics does not represent anything so entirely new in the history of science, other than a new linguistic garb. In 1796, Goethe already formulated the task of physiology in the following way: "All that is wanting for a more rapid development of physiology as a whole, is that one never lose sight of the interaction of all the parts of a living body; for it is only by means of the concept that all the parts of an organic body work upon one part and that each part exerts its influence upon all in turn, that we can hope gradually to fill in the gaps in physiology"; the scientific endeavors that have repeatedly sought to carry Goethe's work further long ago began to strive in this direction. One need only recall, within the context of academia, Smuts (1927), Haldane (1931), Koehler (1933) and Bertalanffy (1932, 1937). Surprisingly—or understandably, depending how one takes it—this approach became acceptable to the "causally-minded" schools only when it became possible to express the unavoidable facts in technomorphic language. Control engineering provided the conceptual structures with a verbal

garb such as "feedback," "regulating unit" and "manip-
ulated variable," "actual value" and "set point," "redun-
dancy" and "signal," "transfer characteristic," "channel
capacity," and "error algorithms"—words that become
technologically graphic when imagined as a circuit diagram.
This would be unobjectionable if such language did not
after all convey more than its mere denotation: adoption of
such verbal forms supplies to a large extent the longed-for
subliminal gratification that cannot be gained from the facts
themselves, namely, that the organism is only a mechanism
after all (see also Fromm 1974, and Schad 1975).

Our self-analysis of scientific thinking must still face the
question: to which of the three modes of thinking we have
described does cybernetics belong? In answering, let us dis-
regard completely mere word-usage and examine instead
the tendency of the thinking itself. Then it becomes clear
that thinking in terms of operational loops will, in the final
analysis, proceed causally as well. Only when cause and effect are conceived as simultaneous can thinking gain direct
access to the living organism, but in cybernetic thinking
cause and effect remain temporally disjunct. The cybernetic
model's rapid succession of causal steps approximates the
simultaneity of the living, but does not capture it. Naturally
one must not overlook the fact that such temporally-extended
operational loops also exist within the organism where the
organism effects its *modus vivendi* by interacting with the
unaltered physical world. But conversely, the cybernetic
model is unable to demonstrate how, without technicians
and entirely on its own, it would steadily evolve, metamorphose and develop further. How can the control function as
such modify itself in an ordered way through time [*in geord-
neter Zeitgestalt*]? No technological operational loop
metamorphoses itself without human intervention; it
creates extended, invariable homeostases for as long as cor-

rosion allows. The organism alters its homeostases continually, and in a way that is both characteristic of the species and temporally ordered (Gut 1971:78–79).

★

An example from the physiology of plasma-growth may clarify what has been said. The conceptual distinction drawn in the past between building-blocks (e.g. simple proteins) and active agents (vitamins, enzymes, hormones) can no longer be uniformly preserved. In the living organism there exist widely distributed substances that fall beneath neither rubric, because they are both building blocks (viewed as mass) and active agents (in their function). What this means is that conditioned and conditioner cannot be sharply distinguished, and thus remain inaccessible to causal analysis: if I change the conditions experimentally, then at the same time I change part of that which is to condition, if not entirely that which is at the same time conditioned. Here cause and effect are as indistinguishable as means and ends. The more the processes tend away from the inorganic and the psychological, and toward the vital, the more each building block becomes an agent and *vice versa*.

Here an alternative mode of explanation must be sought. One must look beyond causal and teleological relationships; one must seek above all the *simultaneous relationships between phenomena*. If one phenomenon occurs, then another related phenomenon necessarily occurs simultaneously. That two phenomena condition and promote one another in turn; that both occur together and by virtue of this are mutually explanatory, is the biological process fundamental to all organisms. The explanations support one another. Yet this mutual illumination does not in any way constitute a circular argument, since circularity is possible only in a situation where an unambiguous temporal distinction can be made, and then overlooked. In the case of living phenomena it is never possible to determine that one phenomenon alone exerts an effect and the other then merely exhibits the consequences. At most it is a matter of relative predominance in the mutual influence. In the ideal case the interaction is so balanced that condition and consequence become identical. The differentiation of the two concepts then becomes irrelevant: now one has to do only with genuine correlates. By virtue of this there consists among all parts of an organism an ongoing interrelationship, the visible evidence of which we term life. It is only through this *simultaneous interrelationship* that every organism appears to us at all times as a whole. Applied to such wholes, the causal and teleological nexus are over-extended conceptual frameworks because they obscure the simultaneous correlation. Thus the word "correlation" is not employed here, as it often is, to signify a relationship not yet submitted to causal analysis, but rather for a relationship that is *simultaneously and mutually conditioning.*

The relationship between living phenomena is, however, not merely simultaneous—in that case it could also be accidental. It is also a necessary one. What criterion do we employ to decide whether this simultaneous interrelationship is necessary? Contemporary thinking requires that each of two criteria be met. One is "inner consistency throughout the whole," as Goethe called it (1784): "The inner consistency throughout the whole makes every creature what it is, and man is man as much through the form and nature of his upper maxilla as he is man through the form and nature of the last part of his little toe."

What is meant here is a correspondence and consistency of structure and form that can be clearly described (Schad 1965), and for which one senses an abundance of evidence. We agree with Bischof (1970), however, that the interpretation of particular cases is not infallible. Thus let us add a second criterion: fruitfulness in the further application of the perceived relationships. Transparency and clarity of internal evidence on the one hand, and on the other, abundant confirmation through being able to solve otherwise insoluble problems are the two truth criteria for the explanatory mode appropriate to the living realm. As long as we are unable to observe the unconscious world of the etheric directly, we experience it at its two boundaries: from the psychological aspect in the experience of evidence, and from the physical aspect in the measure of fruitful application.

★

We can summarize what has been described up to now in the following way. In considering the various modes of thinking we encountered three different kinds, each of which is preferable in one characeristic scientific realm:

causal	*correlative*	*teleological* thinking
physics, chemistry	biology	psychology
mineral-lifeless	living	psychological realm
determined by the past	the present	the future

In scientific thinking we discover an order similar to that obtaining within the three realms of nature themselves. We think differently depending upon the object of our thinking in the world—if we grasp that object correctly. In this way threefold nature demands of our thinking a threefold variety. Thus the natural world is not explicable in terms of *one* way of thinking; in that case it would be schematic. But at the same time it is not merely dualistic; in that case it would consist only of contradictions. Besides the processes that unfold causally and those that are psychological-teleological there is in nature a realm that stands between these, mediates nature's duality through its active presence, and binds the others together without eliminating them: this is the realm of the etheric. It acts as a mediator between the dead and the ensouled aspects of nature.

It is noteworthy in this regard that each realm has a different relationship to time. For lifeless processes time exists only as a "hollow" time segment, e.g. the elapsed time of movement in physics or the speeds of reactions in chemistry. Such segments can for the most part be halted at will and continued again just as well after an interruption of any duration. Time is equally uninteresting in the case of psychological processes because everything is bent upon future goals, the attainment of which is more important than the interim period of time. A life process, however, always proceeds for the sake of its own present. Here time is no longer a mere time segment; rather it is individualized time, time made autonomous in each organism's own life rhythm that cannot be lengthened or shortened at will. Steiner termed this capacity of time the "time body"; this body builds up a species' characteristic form partly in accordance with, and partly in opposition to "external time," just as the spatial body partly opens itself to, and partly isolates itself from the environment.

*

The three kingdoms of nature do not exist side-by-side, for in the final analysis past, present and future also constitute a continuum. Yet an example of the way in which they relate to one another stands before us in every ensouled creature. This is the reason why the organism is so ambiguous. But we may say that its ambiguity is an ordered one and can thus be surveyed in an orderly manner: insofar as the organism is physically present, it can be analyzed in causal terms. Insofar as it lives, it is explicable only in correlative terms. And insofar as it manifests psychological capacities, these are comprehensible teleologically. If we wish to understand the world of living creatures, then our task is to recognize where one can explain causally, where in terms of simultaneous interrelation, and where teleologically.

In their theistic world view, earlier ages plainly had the possibility of experiencing nature, just as it is, as willed by higher worlds. The last centuries, especially the last 150 years, have taught us to exhaust the possibilities of the mechanistic interpretation. Goethe was in a particularly strong position to develop the mode of thinking that does justice to living processes. The essential quality of his scientific thinking is precisely his ability to seek out the interrelations within the present. That is the sense of his words of 1829: "Seek nothing behind the phenomena; they are themselves the theory." In the type of the mammalian skeleton he saw the nexus of parts that simultaneously require one another. In his morphological studies he sought to comprehend the forms in time [*Zeitgestalten*]. Before this "Goethean" mode of thinking there stands today a rich field of possibilities, one cultivated already in many places, but virgin land in many more (see also Hassenstein 1950 and Heisenberg 1967). We speak here frequently of a "Goetheanistic" way of thinking. Yet in the end, Goethean research in the broad sense exists wherever methods adequate to their respective object in nature are employed.

Scientific Thinking in Process

In our consideration of the three modes of scientific thinking, we have thus far sketched each as equally valuable and, as it were, synchronic. Yet in so doing the various areas of research, the dead, the living and the sentient levels of nature are made to appear synchronic as well. Yet we know that all of nature, including man, has arisen out of a common temporal process of development: evolution. Is this temporal dimension not lost in our typological method? The opposite is the case, if we now seek to trace the temporal procedure and course of scientific thinking as well.

Everyone who finds solutions to problems, however trivial, can afterwards observe his train of thought in retrospect. In scientific endeavors such a procedure is often many-faceted and thus capable of being examined in great detail. This requires a certain exertion, for in science much more than in the arts we are inclined to seize upon the result only and to regard the way in which it was obtained as of no consequence, or at least of less consequence than the result. But only when this procedure is also subjected to an inventory and investigation can the scientific attitude of thinking make itself understood and understand itself—the goals we set ourselves at the outset.

In Copei (1960), whose worthwhile collection was undertaken out of pedagogical interest, one finds a series of self-portraits by well-known researchers. Helmholtz reports as follows concerning his "sudden insights" [*glückliche Einfälle*]: "Often enough they sneak into the circle of one's thinking without one's recognizing their importance at first; then occasionally yet another chance circumstance helps one later on to recognize when and under what circumstances they have come—otherwise they are there without one's knowing their origin. In other cases they emerge suddenly, without exertion, like an inspiration. In my experience, they have never come to a tired brain, and never at the desk. I always needed first to have turned all sides of my problem this way and that until I surveyed all its turns and tangles in my mind and could run through them freely, without writing. To get that far without extensive previous work is usually impossible. Then, after the resulting fatigue had passed, an hour of perfect bodily freshness and a quiet feeling of well-being was necessary before the good insights came. Often . . . they were there in the morning upon awakening, as Gauss has also noted. But they were especially wont to come . . . during leisurely climbs upon wooded mountains in sunny weather. . . . The descent was less beautiful when the redeeming insights did not come. Then I could bite into such a question for weeks and months at a time. . . ." (from Copei, following Ostwald 1910:302ff.). Helmholtz described his train of thought, working backwards from the result. How did his thinking transpire going forwards? The process of cognition swings into action through searching and pressing for a solution to a problem that no longer leaves him "cold." Weeks, even months of work are invested, and all known and surmisable ways of solving the problem are run through. This process, is in its whole psychological habitus, *teleological, directed intentionally toward a goal*—the goal of the solution. It can to a large extent be made methodical by means of the "extensive previous work."

Not, however, the process that follows so very differently: the sudden insight. It often comes precisely when one does not force or even expect it; not at one's desk, but rather during a hike in the woods that relaxes, unburdens and calms the soul, or out of sleep. Whence it comes, and how it arises directly out of the work that has gone before, remains mostly obscure. Nevertheless, everything depends upon it; nothing is more welcome. Goethe termed such promptings "aperçus," and described their characteristic features: "It comes over the thinker like an illumination, and the fullness of the particular orders itself before the mind's eye as though of itself, lawfully and interpenetrating" (see Copei 1960:30). Even that which is least expected suddenly closes together in the consciousness of the thinker in a simultaneous order, like a tableau. This process is brought to life by the self-structuring of the genuine *correla-*

tive relationship. For this reason it can be acquired only through practice and not by means of recipe-like instructions.

After a discovery in number theory, Gauss writes: "But all brooding, all seeking was in vain; finally, a few days ago, I succeeded. . . . Just like lightning striking, the riddle solved itself. I myself would not be capable of tracing the thread leading from that which I knew previously, according to which I made my last attempts, and that which enabled me to succeed" (from Copei, following Knapp 1928). And then very characteristically: he would already have the result, if only he knew how to get there.

After having arrived at the conception of the saving insight, we continue on into the beginning of the third process: despite all the work that has gone before, the freshly conceived idea seems premature. Often the appropriate words must first be found. Here begins the work of incorporating the idea into discursive, linear thinking. What were the presuppositions, and what logical chain of thought can be found that afterwards, and indeed every time, reaches the already recognized goal again? Thinkers love to find the most "elegant" (i.e. the shortest) way, but thereby the path originally traversed is usually obscured by the new consciousness. The advantage, however, is that the proof worked out in retrospect is formulated and ensured once and for all, and can as a result be reproduced and employed at will. Thus in this final step the establishment of the *causal mode of thinking* reveals itself to be predominant. Even if this is not necessarily true of the content, it certainly is of the form, since the syntax of a verbal formulation already requires that one thought follow from another in the succession of words.

The process underlying every scientific discovery, however small, exhibits these three steps at least, even if individual researchers place the one or the other in the foreground of consciousness according to their own psychological disposition. One finds further descriptions aplenty in recent research on creativity (Révész 1952 as well as Krech and Crutchfield 1962). As has already been noted, in contemporary scientific thinking the causally formulated end result is universally held to be of the utmost importance. Knowing can easily seem more important than thinking. In the mere transmission of knowledge, [*Wissensvermittlung*] the student often experiences in place of the sufferings and joys of discovery only the spiritually anonymous result. Thus the name "science" [*Wissenschaft*]. A better term for it would be "cognition" [*Erkenntnisschaft*], if it were not so clumsy in German (see also Gegenbaur 1874:2-3). For this reason the above presentation is all the more valuable for fruitful research and teaching. Clearly there are several different organizational levels of the human constitution active in the thinking human being. These we must now distinguish.

For a long enough time, neither materialistic monism nor the most varied dualisms (body/soul or matter/spirit) have helped us advance. In accordance with our experience we can recognize at least four forms of reality. Since 1921 Nicolai Hartmann (1921, 1932, 1940, 1964) has worked out a four-level theory that one still encounters in, e.g., Max Hartmann (1936, 1948), Walter Heitler (1970b, 1974), Konrad Lorenz (1971), Wilhelm Troll (1951) and many of their students. However, we prefer the work of Rudolf Steiner (1904, 1910), because in Hartmann's case the gradations are merely conceptually deduced, while Steiner's rest upon an empiricism both sensory and supersensory.

For the enlightened adult consciousness of today the physically weighable, materially differentiated human body can be clearly perceived by the senses and described in words. The physically quantifiable forms of energy belong to this level as well. Humans share this level with all other natural forms of existence. They have the quality of life in common with the plants. Strangely enough, this latter cannot be reconstructed by the senses directly, but only indirectly in terms of the spatial and temporal ordering that we call an organism. In that we live, we are given from the outset at least unconscious evidence of life within ourselves. The third part of our human nature that we encounter is again more accessible to our waking consciousness: the emotional life of the soul that experiences wishes, pleasure, aversion, aggression, etc. The animals have this in common with us to varying degrees. A characteristic unique to the human being is that which he summons up as consciousness of self and capacity for independent action—even in the face of just those mere feelings of pleasure and aversion. Here one has spoken ever and again of the human personality, the human individuality or spiritual kernel. Steiner named this entity with the simplest German word, one that the individual uses to signify him or herself in every self-identification, however small: the "I." The following terms are commonly employed in anthroposophy for these four parts of the human constitution:

> the I-organization
> the astral organization or sentient body
> the etheric organization, life-body, time-body, or
>   formative-forces-body
> the physical organization or material body

One is struck that the "I" retains its designation in modern language, while the word "astral" stems from medieval and Latin culture, and "etheric" and "physical" are taken over from Greek antiquity—evidently in conjunction with the time period in which a clear consciousness of each developed during cultural history.

The human being alone is capable of scientific thinking.

Thus it proceeds from the human "*I*," and only the "I" can advance it. Only if an "I" steps back in consciousness from everything that it is not itself, is it able to objectify everything else as "the world." What became apparent in the levels of thinking already described was that this separation from the world unleashes the psychic drive to regain—but now consciously—full participation therein. Cognitional striving and curiousity are entirely emotional components (Bischof 1970), which show that work now commences upon the *astral level*. The longer it lasts, the more it is accentuated by displeasure. The next phase passes over into the unconscious life of the *etheric organization*. Just as this etheric organization creates corporeal order in sleep without our knowledge, so here it creates order within cognitional activity, if the problems have previously been posed in a fundamental fashion and one can wait. Here in the time-body the affair "takes its time"—as we note and say quite correctly. A scientist of the previous century who has remained unknown, Peter Heuser, writes in his essay of 1858 "On Sensory and Spiritual Cognition in the Realm of Nature": "A matter is obscure to me, incomprehensible. I engage my powers of thinking, compare, distinguish; still I do not find the truth. Only after several days of further thinking does the truth stand out clearly in my mind. How did it arise within me? Is it perhaps also a spiritual-organic product that requires time to develop, just like the stalk of wheat in the material-organic creation of the wheat kernel?" Thus Heuser cloaks in the form of a question his experience that there are manifestations of life within thinking as well.

But the result is translated into a form that can be retained in memory or learned only when we engage the faculty that thinks as much as possible in causal terms. This latter process is irrevocably dependent upon an intact brain organization, and is thus a function of the *physical body*. When many brain physiologists say that thinking is a function of the brain, they are right insofar as by thinking they usually mean causal thinking. Yet this is only one of several possible modes of thinking. In the case of the other modes, the organs of thinking become those higher parts of the human constitution whose processes are in retrospect much more difficult to recall, but are primarily those that make thinking possible. It is only because they are harder to retain in memory that we often do not know the extent and intensity to which we engage in brain-free thinking (see Steiner 1917:63f.). The brain-bound activities of storage and logical combination can, conversely, be simulated by physical means—if only partially, for the brain is also a living organ. But it is an unscientific begging of the question to proclaim that computers can think, and that the brain is likewise a computer. In the last chapter of Hassenstein's book *Information and Control in the Living Organism* (1965) one finds an enlightening discussion of this point (see also Hassenstein 1966).

In summarizing what has been achieved thus far we might say: In teleological thinking the researcher is active primarily in his or her own astral body; at the correlative level in his or her own etheric body; and in causal thinking with his or her own nervous system. The first level can easily be observed and made methodical through introspection; the last through "extraspection." All the more attractive is the intermediate phase, which, despite being less operable, nevertheless proves especially fruitful if one surveys the process as a whole. The essential characteristic of the etheric body is to unfold its activity, also in thinking, not as linear one-dimensionality, but rather as a two dimensional, tableau-like picture. Allow me to reach for a poetic image to which an unknown epigone of Morgenstern's humoresques turned for help:

Das Augenuh

Palmström hat private Tiere sich erfunden
zu besonderem Umgang in besonderen Stunden.
Von dem Augenuh erfand er gleich ein Pärchen;
sieht wie Reh aus, grau mit Silberhärchen,
und ist etwas unanrührbar Zartes.
Niemand ausser ihm, das weiss er schon, gewahrt es.
Selbst er selbst erlaubt sich selten das Geniessen,
sie im blossen Geist vorsichtig zu begrüssen.
Denn bei zu viel Anbeguck—womöglich gar mit
   Zweck—
werden diese Tiere scheu und laufen weg.

The Augenooh

Palmström has invented private creatures of his own
To occupy himself in quiet hours sitting home.
Of Augenooh he straightway made himself a little pair;
They look like deer a little, only gray with silver hair,
And really are quite delicate and pure.
Nobody else can see them, he is sure.
But he knows he can't indulge himself too often
In mental greetings to them—e'en with precaution.
For when they sense intent in lingering stares,
They run and hide themselves like timid hares.

The wag often captures better than the essayist what cannot
be delivered over to the intellect, what is properly the object
of that "gentle empiricism" (Goethe)—more a "receiving"
than a "grasping"—which demands genuine reverence for
the object of thought.

   We now gain insight into the internal necessity of the
fact that the mode of thinking best suited to the investigation of the physical-inorganic world is the mode that we are
most wont to carry out with our own physical nervous sys-

tem. Upon this rests the success of causal analysis in the cognitional and practical mastery of the physical world in physics, chemistry and their technology. It becomes equally clear that correlative thinking is necessary to an understanding of living objects, because life processes always consist in total interrelationship. In other words: organisms live because they have an etheric organization, and thus they can be grasped only by a thinking that employs its own etheric organization. Where the etheric organization is not employed as an instrument, the living object is missed entirely. The destruction of the environment on a global scale today results from the inability of physical-chemical thinking to make comprehensible the everlasting interaction, the regulative variability of biological equilibria. The phenomena of the psyche, especially those that humans and animals have in common, become comprehensible by means of teleological conceptualization, where, in observing, I transcend the physical and etheric organizations of the animal and am confronted with the immediate workings of the astral. To that end thinking will employ its own astral body, because everything of the nature of desire—whether in the object or in the subject—is always similarly future-oriented.

Result and Prospect

In the approaches to the natural world that have arisen historically, we have identified three forms of thinking that correspond to the manifest order of this existing world. We found moreover that in the full course of the process of cognition the features characteristic to all three capacities for thinking come to light. The first, second or third will step into the foreground, depending on the object. Knowledge of the single human being in his or her unique individuality, however, cannot yet be attained in this way. Our theme is scientific cognition in its entirety, and this science comprehends the human being only insofar as the human is also subsumed beneath unindividuated typologies. This must be expressly emphasized. In conclusion, we turn to address the question of the genetic connections between the three manners of thinking.

Many researchers are irritated by the question whether human thinking can transcend its subjective, alienated character at all. We saw that the incitement to thinking rests upon the separation of the human ego from the world, i.e. upon the separation of subject and object. Attempts at thinking are always subjective at the outset—even if they were already factually in accord with their object, one could not yet decide this conclusively. The process of fruitful cognition consists in overcoming this division. The closer the process of cognition approaches to its goal, the more the sharp division between subject and object disappears. The very possibility of insight into the truth rests precisely upon the experience of the fact that the lawfulness of that which lies outside the "I" emerges within one's own "I" and then no longer remains an alien object. One can say just as well that the "I" rediscovers itself as present within the content of the world (Steiner 1911). True cognition is neither subjective nor objective; rather, it accomplishes precisely the task it has set itself: reaching out to overcome the division. It is universal (Steiner 1894). Thinking heals the wounds that the alienation of humanity from the world has inflicted upon both. That this is possible is not to be wondered at in the end, seeing that humanity had its origin in the same evolutionary process as every other realm of nature. For this reason alone they can never be totally alienated from humanity. Thus cognition is an actively accomplished, conscious reentry into existential, evolutionary union with the content of the world.

The way in which this unification unfolds when accomplished can, in turn, nowhere be experienced more realistically than within the many levels of human nature itself. As nature's most fully developed creature, the human being bears the results of all the previously achieved tableaus of nature's existence within its own organization. More precise observation now shows that division into inorganic, living and sensate realms does not represent a spatial stratification; rather, these are engaged in a reciprocal process whereby one develops out of another, in an "inner"evolution.

Everything we find in the human body by way of lifeless matter such as hair, nails, bone crystalloids, urine, etc., was previously alive; all these originated in metabolism, and display numerous characteristics of their origins, apart from which they cannot be comprehended. Nor is the sphere of life comprehensible in insolation. It is precisely in the human being that one can observe how biological development and health are not givens, but rather depend to a great extent upon psychological dispositon and fundamental well-being. One only need recall those organic disturbances the psychological causes of which have been uncovered by depth psychology and psychosomatics. Recent studies of psycho-hygiene in childhood have made it entirely clear that growth, development and health cannot be ensured through mere care of the body: these biological processes unfold properly only when loving attention, bonding and feelings of security remain intact within the soul (Spitz in Schmalohr 1968).

The accepted view of evolution: lifeless matter—life—sensation, which originated in the theoretical need to simplify the undertaking as much as possible, must be complemented by the evolutionary sequence gained through observation: sensation—living order—lifeless matter. If one compares both aspects of temporal dependence, one sees that influence is exerted in both directions. One can intervene in life processes and sensations for limited periods of time with the help of psycho-chemicals and anabolic drugs, just as, conversely, psychological encouragement and the will to live can have long-term physiological effects.

However, more careful experimental and conceptual analysis brings to light an essential difference. The effect of substances upon psychological and physiological processes always consists in the releasing of faculties latent at a higher level; in no way do these faculties originate from the lower level. One only need recall Spemann's unsuccessful attempt at explanation; irrespective of the specific material, his "organizer" always triggers only those reactions that the salamander embryo has built up during its sensitive periods (Danzer 1966:69–70). And it is well known that psycho-chemicals, hormones and psychedelic drugs only bring to the surface what has long since been present in the soul.

Yet in the other direction one can trace the way in which psychological attitudes, engrained through social practices, pass over into unconscious habits of life and organic well- or ill-being. Everything psychological loses its intentionality when it attains the order it has sought and passes out of the emotional realm into the unconscious realm of the etheric. Similarly, at the next deeper level, excretions of the body arise without exception out of the life context. Thereby the latter evolutionary direction must be valued as decidedly more real.

The main obstacle to the recognition of the three modes of being lay and still lies in their not sharing any single time-quality: rather, as has already been shown, each stands in a different relationship to time, and thus their evolution cannot be imagined simply in terms of the linear succession of physical time. Yet considered in terms of the phenomenology of thinking, this difficulty opens the way to the solution of the problem posed at the outset; we need only weave together all of the motifs we have already elaborated.

Scientific thinking is the search for and reestablishment of the evolved order that has been disintegrated through our having become "I"'s and our attendant alienation from the world. This reestablishment is experienced chiefly where we rediscover the correlative life-orders. In the psychological-emotional realm, we do not discover it immediately; within all pleasure and displeasure, all sympathy and antipathy, we find only the wish, the drive, the striving for a satisfying order which is never that of the moment. Everything astral becomes etheric order only in the future, because only there will it have attained the order it has sought and which alone satisfies thinking. On the other hand, we think of the dying or dead matter within us in causal terms, as proceeding from conditions lying in the past, because the living order in which it originated always lies in the past. In retracing the chain of causes and effects, causal thinking seeks in the final analysis nothing other than the living order out of which the dead has meanwhile fallen, and that alone satisfies thinking here as well.

Anthroposophy demonstrates that the human being is the alphabet whose language the world speaks to us. That which takes place in the day-to-day life of every human being as a kind of microcosmic evolution, stands as an archetypal image of the evolution of the cosmos. Humanity's origins lay in the cosmos of spirit, and in the subsequent stages of evolution humanity allowed the ensouled, living and material worlds to precipitate out of itself. The Middle Ages held worms and flies to be the spontaneous products of dead mud until in 1668 Francesco Redi demonstrated his "omne vivum ex vivo" ("everything living out of the living"). The sixteenth century viewed fossils as "ludi naturae" ("games of nature'') until Leonardo Gessner and others recognized in these stones the remnants of real living creatures. Even the last century held the earth's vast quantities of oil to be of inorganic origin until it could be demonstrated that chlorophyll and hemoglobin were contained therein. It has been established only recently that all chalk sediments are biogenic. Traces of life in the form of organic compounds have been established all the way back into the earliest period of rock formation. Russian geologists hold that "organic life was the main factor determining the evolution of the mineral composition of sedimentary strata" (*Universitas* 1974). Modern natural science has but a short history: future centuries will find further evidence for this emerging trend of finding the origins of the mineral world within the living. Similar relationships between psychological attitudes and living capabilities will likewise be researched more fully as the growing exploitation of the earth's ecosystem transforms the interrelationship between nature and culture from a theoretical problem into a practical one of survival. For today it must be admitted: the decisive impulse has been bequeathed to us by the exclusive and one-sided overvaluation of causal-logical thinking. We must radically rethink science in more productive and differentiated ways if we wish to heal the biosphere of the earth.

Thus, even though the lifeless part of the world is that which has died away, its determinants have their origins in the living order of that world's past. Thus causal thinking can best be applied to this part of the world because, by establishing the backward orientation already out of itself, it seeks unconsciously the past order from which everything stems: the etheric. Since on the other hand everything psychological-astral strives for future wholeness, every teleology indicates already in its very attitude of thought that an order comprehensible to thinking can be attained only from the perspective of the future etheric state which is still in the making. In the face of life itself, causal and teleological thinking prove blunt instruments. The phenomena of life "are themselves the theory." What thinking seeks in the realm of the etheric, it finds just in the immediate, active present, and it is only here that thinking finds it in full. Looking back upon both the other modes of thinking we can say: not only correlative thinking, but all three modes of thinking in science are concerned with the etheric and are themselves the paths to the etheric, to the etheric of the past, of the present, and to that which will become active etherically in the future. This is the life of all thinking.

References

Bertalanffy, L. v. 1932. *Theoretische Biologie*, vol. 1. Berlin: Borntraeger.

— 1937. *Das Gefüge des Lebens*. Leipzig/Berlin: Teubner.

Bischof, N. 1970. "Verstehen und Erklaren in der Wissenschaft vom Menschen." In: M. Lohmann (ed.), *Wohin führt die Biologie? Ein interdisziplinares Kolloquium*. Munich.

Binder, Fritz, and Manfred Kirschner. 1975. "Kirlian-Fotografie, Spuk oder Physik?" *Bild der Wissenschaft* 12(3):38–49.

Bretano, Franz. 1911. *Von der Klassifikation der psychischen Phanomene*. Leipzig.

Cannon, W. B. 1932. *The Wisdom of the Body*. New York: W. W. Norton.

Copei, Friedrich. 1960. *Der fruchtbare Moment im Bildungsprozess*. 5th ed. Heidelberg.

Craig, W. 1918. "Appetites and Aversions as Constituents of Instinct." Biological Bulletin 34:91–107.

Danzer, Albert. 1966. *Fortpflanzung, Entwicklung, Entwicklungsphysiologie*. Heidelberg.

Driesch, Hans. 1908. *The Science and Philosophy of the Organism: The Gifford Lectures, Univ. of Aberdeen, 1907–8*. London: A. and C. Black.

Fromm, Erich. 1973. *The Anatomy of Human Destructiveness*. New York: Holt, Rinehart and Winston.

Gegenbaur, Carl. 1874. *Grundriss der vergleichenden Anatomie*, Einleitung, § 2. Leipzig./ *Elements of Comparative Anatomy*. London: Macmillan.

Goethe, J. W. v. 1784. Letter to Karl Ludwig von Knebel of Nov. 17, 1784. *Sophienausgabe*, sect. IV, vol. 6, p. 390, letter no. 2009. Weimar 1890.

— 1796. "Vorträge uber die drei ersten Kapitel des Entwurfs einer allgemeinen Einleitung in die vergleichende Anatomie, ausgehend von der Osteologie." *dtv-Gesamtausgabe*, vol. 37, p. 101. Munich 1962.

— 1829. "Betrachtungen im Sinne der Wanderer." *dtv-Gesamtausgabe*, vol. 18, p. 57. Munich 1962.

Gut, Bernardo. 1971. *Informationstheorie und Erkenntnislehere.* Dornach.

Haeckel, Ernst. 1917. *Kristallseelen: Studien uber das anorganische Leben.* Leipzig.

Haldane, John Scott. 1931. *The Philosophical Basis of Biology: Donnellan Lectures, Univ. of Dublin, 1930.* Garden City N.Y.: Doubleday, Doran & Co.

Hartmann, Max. 1936. "Wesen und Wege biologischer Erkenntnis." *Die Naturwissenschaften* 24:705-13.

— 1948. *Die philosophischen Grundlagen der Naturwissenschaften.* 2nd ed. Stuttgart 1959.

Hartmann, Nicolai. 1921. *Grundzüge einer Metaphysik der Erkenntnis.* 5th ed. Berlin 1965.

— 1932. *Das Problem des geistigen Seins.* 2nd ed. Berlin 1949.

— 1940. *Ontologie 3: Der Aufbau der realen Welt.* 2nd ed. Meisenheim 1949.

— 1942. *Neue Wege der Ontologie.* 4th ed. Stuttgart 1964./*New Ways of Ontology.* Westport, Conn.: Greenwood Press 1975.

Hassenstein, Bernhard, 1950. "Goethes Morphologie als selbstkritische Wissenschaft und die heutige Gültigkeit ihrer Ergebnisse." *Jahrbuch der Goethe-Gesellschaft* (Weimar) N.F. 12:333-57.

— 1965. *Biologischer Kybernetik.* Heidelberg./ *Information and Control in the Living Organism: An Elementary Introduction.* London: Chapman and Hall 1971.

— 1966. "Kybernetic und biologische Forschung." *Handbuch der Biologie* vol. 1, pp. 626-717. Frankfurt.

Heisenberg, Werner. 1967. "Das Naturbild Goethes und die technisch-naturwissenschaftliche Welt." *Jahrbuch der Goethe-Gesellschaft* (Weimar) N. F. 29:27-42.

Heitler, Walter. 1970a. *Naturphilosophische Streifzüge.* Braunschweig.

— 1970b. "Die Physik und die Lebensvorgänge." *Universitas* 25(5):533-38.

— 1974. "Stufen der Belebung und der unverwesliche Leib." In: H. Zoller (ed.), *Die Befreiung vom wissenschaftlichen Glauben.* Freiburg i. Brsg.

Heuser, Peter. 1858. "Ueber sinnliche und geistige Erkenntnis auf dem Gebiete der Natur." *Jahresbericht des naturwissenschaftlichen Vereins von Elberfeld und Barmen*, pp. 105-116. Elberfeld.

Kipp, Friedrich. 1949. "Arterhaltung und Individualisierung in der Tierreihe." *Verhandlungen der Deutschen Zoologen in Mainz*, pp. 23-27. Mainz.

Knapp, Konrad. 1928. "Mathematik und Kultur." *Preussische Jahrbuch* (Berlin) 211(3):298ff.

Koehler, Otto. 1933. "Das Ganzheitsproblem in der Biologie." *Schriften der Königsberger Gelehrten Gesellschaft, Naturwissenschaftliche Klasse* (Halle/Saale) 9(7):137-204.

Krech, D. and R. S. Crutchfield. 1962. *Elements of Psychology*. New York.

Lorenz, Konrad. 1937. "Ueber die Bildung des Instinktbegriffes." *Die Naturwissenschaften* 25:19ff. Reprinted in: *Ueber tierisches und menschliches Verhalten – aus dem Werdegang der Verhaltenslehre*, vol. 1. Munich 1966./ *Studies in Human and Animal Behaviour*. Cambridge: Harvard Univ. Press, 1970-71.

— 1971. "Der Mensch, biologisch gesehen." *Studium generale* 24(4):495-515.

Matile, Philipp. 1973. "Die heutige entscheidende Phase in der biologischen Forschung. *Universitas* 28(5):543-558.

Ostwald, Wilhelm. 1910. *Grosse Manner*. Leipzig.

Overhage, Paul. 1965. *Die Evolution des Lebendigen – Die Kausalität*. Freiburg i.Br.

Peters, H. M. 1972. "Historische, soziologische und erkenntniskritische Aspekte der Lehre Darwins." In: H. G. Gadamer and P. Vogler (eds.), *Neue Anthropologie, vol. 1: Biologische Anthropologie, part 1*, pp. 326-52. Stuttgart.

Rein, Hermann and Max Schneider. 1964. *Physiologie des Menschen*. 5th ed. Berlin.

Rensch, Bernhard. 1968. *Biophilosophie auf erkenntnistheoretischer Grundlage*. Stuttgart./ *Biophilosophy*. New York: Columbia Univ. Press, 1971.

Révész, G. 1952. *Talent und Genie*. Munich.

Schad, Wolfgang. 1965. "Stauphänomene am menschlichen Knochenbau." *Elemente der Naturwissenschaft* 3:15-27.

— 1966. "Biologisches Denken." *Elemente der Naturwissenschaft* 5:10-19.

— 1975. "Anatomie der Zerstorung." *Die Drei* 45(3):124-127. [Review of Fromm 1973.]

— 1977. *Man and Mammals*. Garden City N.Y.: Waldorf Press.

Schilder, F. A. 1952. *Einführung in die Biotaxonomie*. Jena.

Schmalohr, Emil. 1968. *Frühe Mutterentbehrung bei Mensch und Tier. Entwicklungspsychologische Studie zur Psychohygiene der frühen Kindheit*. Munich and Basel.

Smuts, J. C. 1927. *Holism and Evolution*. London.

Spranger, Eduard. 1924. *Psychologie des Jugendalters*. 20th ed. Heidelberg 1949.

Steiner, Rudolf. 1894. *The Philosophy of Freedom*. Spring Valley N.Y.: Anthroposophic Press 1964.

— 1904. *Theosophy: An Introduction to the Supersensible Knowledge of the World and the Destination of Man.* Spring Valley N.Y.: Anthroposophic Press 1971.

— 1910. *An Outline of Occult Science.* Spring Valley N.Y.: Anthroposophic Press 1972.

— 1911. "The Psychological Foundations of Anthroposophy." (Lecture at the Fourth Intern. Philosophical Congress in Bologna, Italy, April 8, 1911.) In: *Esoteric Development: Selected Lectures and Writings from the Works of Rudolf Steiner.* Spring Valley N.Y.: Anthroposophic Press 1982.

— 1917. *The Case for Anthroposophy.* London: Rudolf Steiner Press 1970.

— 1922. *Konferenzen Rudolf Steiners mit den Lehren der Freien Waldorfschule in Stuttgart 1919-1924.* GA 300b, 1975. Conference of June 21, 1922.

Strombach, W. 1968. *Natur und Ordnung.* Munich.

Suchantke, Andreas. 1974. "Biotoptracht und Mimikry bei afrikanischen Tagfaltern." *Elemente der Naturwissenschaft* 21:1-21.

Troll, Wilhelm. 1951. "Das Analogieproblem in seiner Bedeutung fur die Naturerkenntnis." *Experientia* 7:11. Reprinted in: *Neue Hefte zur Morphologie* (Weimar), no. 2 (1956), pp. 47-63.

Universitas. 1974. Vol. 4, p. 435; vol. 8, p. 883; vol. 11, p. 1221.

Life Organization and Thought Organization:
Concerning the Dual Nature of the Human Etheric Body
Christof Lindenau

The investigation of any area of the world presupposes that the investigator be equipped with the organs and tools, apparatus, equipment, etc. which correspond to the area in question. In short, he must possess the methodological means whereby the area may be rendered accessible. We would try in vain, for instance, to ascertain the weight of a glass of water by means of a thermometer or to measure its temperature with a balance; not because balance and thermometer are unreliable instruments, but because a thermometer is appropriate solely for measuring an object's state of warmth and a balance for determining its weight. This obvious requirement that the research equipment be appropriate to the object under investigation holds true as well for the realm of the etheric. Here, too, research must be accompanied by careful reflection upon the means and implements which it employs.

One question in particular is of concern in this connection: is there anything in man's own makeup which provides him with independent access to this realm, just as the organization of his sense of hearing, for instance, gives him access to the realm of acoustical phenomena? Or must he content himself with inferring the existence of a world of etheric forces merely on the basis of apparatus and experimental undertakings of his own devising? The following discussion seeks to contribute to the answering of this question by describing what aspect of the etheric world impinges on the human being and is therefore also capable of becoming an organ for the perception of that world.

Anthroposophical science of the spirit shows that each human being bears a portion of the etheric world individualized within himself. Rudolf Steiner refers to this part of the etheric world which impinges upon each human being as the human "etheric body" or "body of formative forces."[1] We are only able to use our physical body as an instrument in the physical world because it is an integral part of that world. Similarly, our etheric body can only become an instrument for the investigation of the etheric world by virtue of the fact that it belongs both to ourselves and to that world of etheric formative forces.

It is in many respects its spatial attributes which render our physical body a suitable instrument for the physical, sensory world. These attributes refer both to its own spatial extension and to its numerous connections with the surrounding world of space. On the one hand we find that each organ such as the eye, ear and sense of touch places us in a different connection to our spatial surroundings. On the other hand this spatial orientation is exemplified by the movements of our limbs in space. The physical body thus has a direct relationship to space. The etheric body has a similarly direct relationship to time. Just as we experience the physical body primarily as a spatially organized structure, so too may we come to know the etheric body most readily in its temporal organization. It is, in short, a temporal body, just as the physical is a spatial body.

The integration of the physical body into the element of time comes to expression in the rhythm of growth and dissolution which is present, for instance, in the sense organs and limbs mentioned above. This integration of the physical into the stream of time does not belong fundamentally to the physical body but rather to the etheric body. The etheric body permeates the physical body from birth (or conception) to death and organizes in it all its characteristic processes of life, such as nourishment, growth, reproduction etc. An examination of the "life organization" active in these processes thus also provides insight into the structure of the etheric body. Since knowledge of this structure is important for the understanding of the etheric body as an organ for the investigation of the etheric world, we shall proceed first to an examination of this side of the etheric body, the side which is directed toward the physical body.

When we study the physical body of man with respect to its life processes "our attention is first drawn to the process whereby the inner life of the body is sustained from without." This is how Rudolf Steiner begins his discussion of these matters in a fragmentary work entitled "Anthroposophy" (1910). With respect to the breathing process he continues: "In this process the life of the body comes into contact with the outer world; in a sense it confronts the outer world in a condition in which it cannot continue, in order to receive from the outer world the strength to perpetuate itself."[2]

This applies not only to the inhaling of air, however, but also to all the other processes of "taking in" associated with bodily life. Thus, for instance, solid and liquid nourishment must first be taken in from the surrounding world before they, in their further course of transformation, may impart to the body the strength for its continued existence. The processes of taking in are now joined by others which "adjust" the newly acquired substances to the bodily life. For instance, they warm and moisten the newly inhaled air and transform solid food through mastication and salivation. In a similar way, however, the bodily life also continually adjusts itself to its own conditions, as in the process whereby it penetrates all its limbs and organs with a definite degree of warmth which is independent of the external temperature.

A third kind of process is connected particularly with nourishing, inasmuch as through digestion, all which has been taken in and adjusted to the body is chemically dissolved and destroyed—particularly in the stomach and intestinal tract—and the elements useful for life separated from those of no consequence. Since the digestive process takes place differently in the case of the various substances we have to do here with a plurality of processes, all of which are nevertheless active in similar ways in the physical body.

With respect to the three different activities of the etheric body underlying the processes we have thus far discussed, we may speak here of *taking in, adjusting* and *digestion.* (In the foregoing discussion Rudolf Steiner uses other terminology and instead of these three expressions speaks of "breathing," "warming" and "nourishing." This would seem, at least in respect to the first instances, to be related to the fact that in each case he wished to point to just that form of the corresponding life process in which the spiritual physiognomy of this process is imaged most vividly.) The manifold digestive processes, in turn, could not take place were not the etheric body to become active in a fourth way in the physical body—through *secretion,* e.g. of gastric or pancreatic juice etc.—and thus effect digestion by sending from within the life of the body something which goes forth to meet the substances which have been taken in and adjusted. This outwardly-directed processof secretion is complemented by one directed inwardly toward the life of the body itself insofar as the blood circulation secretes substances into the various tissues of the bodily organs. Here the substances then serve three further activities of the etheric body: *sustenance, growth* and *reproduction.*

In contrast to the first three activities these last three are directly connected with the life of the physical body itself. In the processes of sustenance the substances secreted from the general stream of nourishment are transformed by the etheric body into the substance of specific organs, in order that what is used up each day in these various organs may be continually replaced. In all the processes of growth, however, something new is added to what is already present. The new substance is thereby altered with respect to its size and weight and also to the relation of the bodily organs to one another and to the degree of their maturity. In the case of sustenance and growth the activity of the etheric body is still limited to the immediate physical body. In the process of reproduction it transcends this body as a new body is brought forth. A new living being arises in the womb of the old. The further elaboration or renewal observed already in the process of sustenance and growth here becomes all-encompassing.

★

When we contemplate the various modes of activity of these processes which make of the human physical body a living entity, we thus find in them seven different fundamental tendencies. In reference to them one may speak of the "seven life processes" in which the etheric body unfolds its activity with respect to the physical body. Further reflection now shows that these seven life processes are not related to one another merely by virtue of their mutual activity in the orchestration of the unified physical corporeality, but also by virtue of their already having themselves originated in a totality—that of the etheric body. By calling forth this totality in inward contemplation, we draw a step closer to the essential being of the etheric body. How may we take this step?

In the foregoing discussion the three processes of sustenance, growth and reproduction, which are oriented toward the body, were juxtaposed with those of taking in, adjusting and digestion, which are oriented toward the surrounding world. The process of secretion provides a mediating activity between these two groups. This preliminary juxtaposition may be extended as we in turn compare each process in the one group with the corresponding process in the other.

Let us once again begin with the process of "taking in." Its function is to introduce into the life of the body something which previously had belonged to the surrounding world (breath, nourishment, etc.). The reverse is accomplished by a life process which, through birth, brings a new living being into the world and thereby places into the surroundings something which previously had belonged to the life of the body. In this respect reproduction thus shows itself to be a *reversed* "taking in." Moreover, similar connections may be shown to obtain between adjusting and growth, digestion and sustenance.

The simple introduction of a foodstuff into the physical body, for instance, does not yet suffice actually to integrate it into the bodily life. Although it is then spatially present in the human body, in essence it still belongs to the surroundings. Only through "adjustment" with respect to its physical characteristics (through mastication, salivation, warming) is it lead over effectively into the life of the body. Without this adjustment, that which has been taken in represents a foreign body which weighs down this life and which is ejected as soon as possible—if necessary violently, by vomiting. Similarly, the newborn infant finds itself spatially in the outside world, but still belongs essentially with the life of its mother. This is evidenced not only by the fact that it must continue to be nourished by this life but also, for instance, by the fact that the size and weight of its limbs in proportion to one another and to the surroundings are still altogether unfavorable for life in the outside world. Thus the limbs, for instance, are much too small and too light in relation to the head, so that the body cannot move about effectively in the physical world, etc. On the other hand they are definitely accommodated to life in the body of the mother. The real accomplishment of the growth process thus becomes evident here. Growth is not a merely additive procedure. It is, rather, one which transforms those proportions which are suited to life in the maternal body into those which are suited to the surroundings. The child grows into its environment. When viewed in this way the process of growth appears as a reversed process of adjusting: an adjustment to the world.

The same may be said with respect to digestion and sustenance. What has been taken in from the environment and adjusted to the warm semifluid condition of the physical body, still retains in its biological, or at least in its chemical, structure the character of the surrounding world. For it was built up by that world. Digestion now destroys this entity by annihilating and casting out every bit of it which is not compatible with what is present in the human body. The opposite occurs in the case of sustenance. For in a manner which is the exact inverse of digestion, the sustaining process takes up its task of rebuilding at just that point at which life in the surroundings has used up and destroyed something in the body. Here it replaces the destroyed substances with new ones which are integrated into the life of specific organs. By complementing or replacing what is present in man, the sustaining process holds back the destructive influence of the surroundings. In this respect regeneration may therefore be understood to be the result of a "reversed" digestive process.

Digestion suppresses those aspects of the food which are connected with the outside world, in order that specific substances may be formed in the course of the body's further development. In the context of our present approach, we first encountered such specific substances in the saliva, gas-

tric juices and various stomach enzymes, i.e. in the outwardly directed secretion of those substances which work
chemically upon what has been taken in as nourishment.
Similarly, however, the inwardly directed secretion, such as
that at work in the activity of the liver, forms specific
human substances which it then places at the disposal of the
formation of the tissues of specific organs through the processes of sustenance, growth, etc. The specific substances
formed in the realm of secretion are therefore destined on
the one hand for destruction and on the other for renewal.
Through its devotion to the other life processes the process
of secretion is thus reversed *within itself.* But especially
when we focus our attention on that "endocrine" secretion
["*Insonderung*"] which through the glands and neuro-
hormones *regulates* the various kinds of secretion [*Absonder-
ung*] we have discussed, it becomes clear that this process is
not simply a single life process in a sequence of seven. On
the contrary it simultaneously occupies a unique position
among them, a position whose significance transcends all
the others. Through its regulating activity it emerges as the
"heart" of the sevenfold life organization.

Among the experiences one can have in working one's
way actively into this thought-complex, are two which are
directly connected with spiritual research. One has to do
with the experience of thinking: the more intensely we im-
merse ourselves in these metamorphoses and reverse transformations of the life processes, the more we experience our
thinking to be borne by a harmony of spiritual movements.
While we were previously obliged always to support our
thought with sensory observation we now find within
thought itself that which supports and carries it. And gradually, through the observation of the movements of thinking, the harmony of which we have spoken transforms itself
into an inner experience in imagery—an experience of

strange and austere beauty. Such an experience is not insignificant if we wish to find the way from the field of experience determined by natural science to that of the science of the spirit.

For purposes of describing the independence which we wish to attain in the life of the soul as it is immersed in thinking, we may, for instance, point to the use we have made of the number seven. Out of the nature of everyday thinking it is understandable that this number, supported by just as many groups of facts observed by the senses, had first of all to be conceived in the sense of an enumeration. In the course of our investigation it became clear, however, that we are not concerned here merely with a "number of pieces" but with an inwardly articulated whole. From the point of view taken here, the whole is characterized by the number seven. If we compare what was said above concerning the threefold nature of secretion, however, we find that from another point of view the whole is properly characterized by the number nine. Therefore, if the reality of the life organization is to be grasped spiritually, it is necessary to speak not of seven life processes but of a *sevenfoldness* of such processes. It is clear, however, that the term "sevenfoldness" is understood here not as the mystically nebulous vagary of a long-since corrupted tradition but rather as a spiritual organism, an organism of self-sustained movements of thought, an organism which as such is capable of being *observed* in thinking.

The other experience which one has in connection with this spiritual research is related to the fact that in devoting attention repeatedly to such inner experiences, the movements of thought engaged in this activity become organs or instruments of spiritual attentiveness, very much as eyes and ears are instruments of sensory attentiveness. Through the new spiritual organs one may begin to lead one's research into new spheres. Whereas it is initially bound to sense observation it may now be expanded into realms such as the etheric, which form the supersensible basis for the world of the senses. On this new path those things which traditional sense-bound research had described as individual facts, now show themselves to be embedded in an activity which can be investigated only by spiritual research.

This is also true for the investigation of another side of the etheric body. Through this side the etheric body forms the basis not only for man's physical existence but also for his life of soul. While this is a question of importance not only for education but for the entire cultural life, it was especially in connection with pedagogical matters that Rudolf Steiner spoke and wrote to this point. He drew attention to the fact that during childhood a portion of the etheric body releases itself from its activity in the physical body and is henceforth at the disposal of the activity of the soul. This event is essentially completed with the full emergence of the second or permanent set of teeth. The beginnings of the second dentition may therefore serve as a bodily indicator of the emerging readiness for school.[3] The child might of course also have formal instruction prior to this point, but this is accomplished only by drawing prematurely on those forces which the child still needs for the forming of a healthy body. A weakening of physical health is therefore the necessary consequence.

From this point on, however, it is essential that the learning processes begin. For it is precisely through this liberated part of the etheric body that man is by nature predisposed to become a cultural being. In all of these changes it is therefore not simply a question of a partial freeing of the etheric body *from* something, i.e. from the life of the body, but also of a freeing *for* something: for the life of the soul itself within the processes of thought, feeling and volition.[4]

Just as this life of the soul requires the foundation of the physical body for its healthy development, so also does it require the foundation which the etheric body offers it by placing a portion of its forces at the soul's disposal. This portion will now be discussed insofar as it can be comprehended by means of the thoughts first gleaned through a study of the bodily activity of the etheric and then remolded into organs of a subtler awareness. The discussion will focus in particular upon the thinking, cognizing activity of soul in man.

*

Among the processes which in a larger or narrower sense are connected with the cognitive life we must first of all count sense perception. Through the senses man continually receives from the environment the stimuli not only for his cognitive life but for his life of soul in general. Yet these perceptions are actually available to the soul only to the extent that we are able to recall them. For this activity perception alone does not suffice. It belongs more to the world than to ourselves. Only in the forming of memories do we begin to lead perception over into the realm of our own life of soul. To be sure, the mental digestion of perceptions and observations requires that one be able to do more than simply remember them. The world comes toward us through perception, but we do not leave it in the form in which it first presents itself. We break it down into its component parts. Every analytical process bears witness to this fact. We cannot really make anything our own without constantly distinguishing true from false, useful from useless, essential from non-essential.

In this way one may begin to demonstrate that that portion of the etheric body which now serves as the foundation for the cognitive life possesses a structure similar to that portion which continues its activity in the physical body. In perception we easily rediscover the quality of "taking in," and in memory-formation that of "adjusting." For just as this process of adjusting, for instance, conveys what has been taken in as nourishment into the range of the bodily life, so do memory-formation and the recollection based on it convey perceptions into the range of the life of soul. And in the analytical activity of intellectual thought we recognize once more the "analytical" character of digestion.

With this the task of thought is not exhausted, however. Thinking can undertake to reconnect what has become separated, to reassemble the details into a whole, to attain an overview and to integrate new knowledge into its own world of thought. And thus, for instance, we have need of a thinking which creates relationships and grasps totalities, if we are to evolve a clear understanding of what has been described above as the sevenfold organism of the life processes. This thinking thereby shows itself to be a reversal of analytical thought just as regeneration may be termed a "reversed digestion."

What emerges in this way as an experience in absolutely pure thinking, can, however, also become the beginning of a new path for man's striving for knowledge. We have suggested that thoughts, properly cultivated, can become instruments of heightened awareness. How does this happen? We found that that thinking which grasps totalities may in certain respects be understood as a reversal of the thinking which distinguishes differences. Here, too, the matter depends upon a reversal: a kind of "reversed memory-formation." In ordinary memory-formaton the perception must of course first be present before it can be recalled to mind. Memory thus creates in man a kind of "after-image" of that perceptual image which belongs to the world. In the case of our present discussion of the emergence of organs of perception for the supersensible world, however, we have to do with the opposite: the cultivation of a "fore-image," i.e. of an image which must be created in man *prior to* the perception of the corresponding supersensible reality. In part this cultivation consists in meditative devotion to such mental pictures [*Vorstellungen*] as those developed above with respect to the human life-organization. While these mental pictures seem at first to rest exclusively upon a "constructing" power of thought altogether separate from the other forces of the soul, they gradually acquire a life of their own, a life which works back upon and transforms the forces of feeling and volition. In the course of these processes, however, precisely the same activity occurs which was described above as the process of growth, except that now it is a question of growth not into the physical world but into the spiritual world. We no longer think "about" the world—our thinking itself becomes the organ through which the world may be experienced in its spiritual content.[5]

Supersensible cognition and that mediated by the senses differ fundamentally, of course, through the manner in which they occur. In the realm of the senses we must set about finding externally the object or process we wish to learn to know, in order to be able to observe it. It exists in the world as a spatially separate entity, and we ourselves also assume a position opposite it while observing it. In the realm of supersensible experience this is different. From the start we find ourselves inwardly, i.e. intuitively at one with it and now stand before the task of separating it creatively from ourselves in a free formative process, in order to become conscious of it. This formative process can take place in various ways: in the forming of new thought-images, in the creation of a work of art, in practical social action. *How* it takes place is understandably a factor of the difference in human individualities. The *content* of what is revealed in the process, however, has nothing to do with this difference. It has to do with the worlds with which the individual in question is intuitively connected through schooling and destiny. What comes into existence from out of this world through a human being also endures independently of him, just as every human being is a child of his parents and yet also an independent being who, before birth, belonged to the very same spiritual worlds which can be investigated through supersensible experience.

In this way one can discover that the cognitive life of man has at its disposal not only a physical but also an etheric "thought organization" whose structure corresponds completely to that found to underlie the life organization. We may add that the thought organization has its actual center in that part of the etheric body through which *interest* manifests itself as a universal psychological force. Within the cognizing life of the soul we have to do especially with a particular form of this force: questioning. In the case of the life of the body we were able to speak of a sevenfold organization. We may thus also do so here:

Life Organization	*Thought Organization*
taking in	perception
adjusting	memory
digestion	distinguishing
secretion	questioning
sustenance	grasping totalities
growth	becoming an organ
reproduction	formation

Here one may notice how again within the thought organization the process of questioning is itself oriented toward two sides, just as is the process of secretion within the life organization. For we can just as well inquire about differences as about relationships. At the same time we can observe that when we pose questions concerning our own being this process finds its center.

An extended discussion would show among other things that the process of "becoming an organ" takes place not only through meditation proper, but also in every instance in which we occupy ourselves long and intensely enough with a thought and, testing its possible applications, carry it toward the physical or spiritual world. It is just that in meditation this carrying of the thought toward the world, toward the spiritual world, is done consciously.

*

As was emphasized at the beginning of this study, research into each specific area of the world requires instruments of investigation which are appropriate to that area. For the etheric world the first of these instruments may be sought in the thought organization which this area of the world has built into man. (Further instruments also become available on the paths of inner development which Rudolf Steiner describes.) Insofar as our thinking is able to use this thought organization it possesses innate access to the etheric world, just as for instance the sense of hearing possesses innate access to the world of acoustical phenomena through the organization of the outer, middle and inner ear. The first task in this area thus consists in grasping and working through one's own etheric thought organization as an encompassing instrument for gaining knowledge of the etheric world. We spoke earlier about the way in which such a grasping and working through can be accomplished. In order that one may apply this instrument cognitively in specific instances within or outside of man, one will need on the one hand to transform specific thoughts derived from the study of the life processes into organs directed attentively toward the etheric realm. And on the other hand one will need to elaborate creatively those intuitions which one has gained through the use of such organs.

Whether the thought organization becomes an instrument of research for the etheric realm of the world, or whether it evolves forms of thinking which are appropriate only to material reality and through this one-sidedness alienates itself from its origin depends, therefore, on the use to which we put it. If one adds to this the fact that the world of the etheric is but one of the spiritual domains of which spiritual research speaks, one finds that another task becomes visible from this vantage point. It has to do with a refinement of scholarly-scientific study such that the student is enabled to understand the cosmos with equal precision from both spiritual and material points of departure and thereby to acquire an encompassing world view. From a study of the etheric nature of man such as we have sketched here, one may derive important intimations as to how one might proceed in developing forms of scientific study both individually and in concert with others.[6]

As a third task which becomes evident here, one may mention the further investigation of the connection between that part of the human etheric body which is active in the physical body and that part which becomes available for the life of the soul. It is clear that this area of the study of etheric man embraces at least the entire domain of education, including both preschool and school, as well as its corresponding hygienic aspects.[7] Thus, for instance, we find that for the first seven years of man's development the process of taking in assumes a supreme importance, for the second seven years the process of acquisition through memory and for the third seven years the process of analytic thought and judgment. With respect to the first seven years Rudolf Steiner speaks of the fact that in the forms of the surrounding world as the child perceives them, there lies something which has a direct effect on the formation of the child's body. For what inheres in the forms affects the child in the manner of an impulse of growth, now furthering, now impeding the child's developing life in accordance with the nature of the various forms themselves.[8] With respect to the second seven years he points to a corresponding relationship inasmuch as excessive demands on the memory have effects on bodily growth other than do excessive claims on the imagination.[9] But how may such phenomena be understood out of the dual nature of man's etheric body? The point in time which essentially separates the development of the second seven-year period from that of the first was also discussed above as the point of emerging readiness for school. And it was noted that the etheric life forces may also be drawn away from the body too soon, with the resulting predisposition to illness. But the opposite can also occur: if the soul does not take hold properly of those life forces which place themselves at its disposal after this point in time, these forces, too, will generate tendencies toward illness. Both dangers to the growing human being are thus related to the cultural side of the human etheric body: they arise when this cultural side does not emerge or is not cultivated at the appropriate time, but either too early or too late.

Finally we may point to a fourth area of life and research which can also emerge as a task in addition to the foregoing. It has to do with art: the creation and contemplation of art and the related sphere of hygienic-therapeutic activity. A further investigation of that portion of the etheric body which is available to the life of the soul would demonstrate that this portion does not only take part in the soul's cognitional activity. It is also intensely active in all artistic endeavor, with respect both to the study and appreciation of art as well as to its creation.[10] It is therefore obvious that one must look within the dual nature of man's etheric body for the basis of the hygienic-therapeutic application and effectiveness of artistic work. From a study of man worked out for this area, we should be able to proceed to evolve practical impulses, beginning with architecture and working right on into the formation of our entire cultural environment.

Notes

References to untranslated works of Rudolf Steiner are given by GA number (GA = Gesamtausgabe = Collected Edition, published by Rudolf Steiner Verlag, Dornach, Switzerland).

1. Steiner, R. *Theosophy* (1904). Spring Valley, N.Y.: Anthroposophic Press 1964. Chapter 1, section 1.

2. Steiner, R. *Anthroposophie, Ein Fragment* (1910). GA 45, 2nd ed. 1970.

3. Steiner, R. *The Education of the Child in the Light of Anthroposophy* (1907). 2nd ed. London: Rudolf Steiner Press 1965.

4. Steiner, R. *Spiritual Science and Medicine* (1920). London: Rudolf Steiner Press 1948. Lecture of March 23, 1920.

5. For a discussion of the nature of the meditative work intended here, see Steiner, R. *Knowledge of the Higher Worlds and Its Attainment* (1904). 3rd ed. Spring Valley, N.Y.: Anthroposophic Press 1947, and *An Outline of Occult Science* (1910). 3rd ed. Spring Valley, N.Y.: Anthroposophic Press 1972.

6. Lindenau, C. *Der übende Mensch.* Stuttgart: Verlag Freies Geistesleben 1976.

7. Compare Schad, W. "Menschenkundliche Anmerkungen" in: M. Strauss (ed.) *Von der Zeichensprache des kleinen Kindes.* Stuttgart: Verlag Freies Geistesleben 1976.

8. See note 3.

9. Steiner, R. *Study of Man* (1919). London: Rudolf Steiner Press 1966. Lecture of September 2, 1919.

10. Steiner, R. *Das Rätsel des Menschen* (1916). GA 170, 2nd ed. 1978. See especially the lecture of August 15, 1916.

The Concept and Action of the Etheric Body[1]
Hermann Poppelbaum

Focussing on a single part of the human being, such as the etheric body, is always problematic because each part interacts with others. Thus, we cannot strictly limit ourselves to our theme, but must to some extent also include the neighboring parts.

Even in the plant, which anthroposophically oriented spiritual science describes as twofold (consisting of a physical and an etheric body), it is not possible to describe the etheric body in isolation. One must elucidate how its activities counteract those of the physical body, how it raises the substance of the plant out of the context of the inorganic and keeps it from sinking back into the realm of the purely physical until the moment of death.

One must also, however, relate the etheric body of the plant to a higher realm. Those forces which Rudolf Steiner describes as "astral" (see below, p. 233)—which come from the periphery and transform mere vitality into sentience—they too express themselves within the etheric body of the plant. They modify and direct the phases of its activity, and they specialize its forms.

In man the etheric body is similarly impinged upon, except that the astral is not present as forces from the periphery, but as part of man's being, his astral body. Furthermore, the physical, etheric and astral bodies are infused with an ego, or "I," which again is quite different from the other three members of man's being. Rudolf Steiner once contrasted the etheric body and the astral body as the "functional" and the "functioning," and then defined the ego as the "pulsating" within the "functioning."[2] Descriptions of anything "functional" must always be incomplete because they omit the functioning agent. For this reason, descriptions of the etheric body in isolation suffer from a kind of anonymity. To be really complete, a spiritual scientific account must always be pursued to the agent whose activity underlies the phenomenon. This must be kept in mind in the following sections.

The Etheric Body as a Functional Totality

Since it cannot be perceived with the physical senses, but only with higher senses,[3] the etheric body is accessible to ordinary consciousness only in the form of thought (as concept or idea). Nevertheless, for our purposes it is best to start by recalling how the etheric body appears to supersensible perception. With deliberate realism, Rudolf Steiner characterized it thus:

> The streaming movements of the etheric body maintain the form and condition of all the organs of the physical body. Underlying the physical heart is an "etheric heart," underlying the physical brain as an "etheric brain," etc. . . . . Whereas in the physical body separate organs are present, in the etheric body everything is in living, interpenetrating flow.[4]

When making the transition in thought from the physical body to the etheric body, one must overcome the conception of the organs having fixed contours and imagine a lively interplay of processes. But this interweaving should not induce one to let the concept itself become blurred or inexact. Although the interplay of processes is constantly changing, at a given time and place it is always definite and concrete. One could perhaps object that the physiological concept of an "interplay of functions" already takes ordi-

nary reality sufficiently into account, so that a special concept of the etheric body is not needed. And yet, when one
thinks of such an interplay of functions, one is thinking
about the etheric body only from the outside, instead of
grasping its essence. Although isolated functions may be a
necessary fiction for research, they do not exist in the living
reality. An individual function can only be separated in
thought from the functional totality; it presupposes this
totality, which is a reality and not the sum of its parts. Just
as contemporary psychology has overcome the fiction of individual sensations (and become Gestalt psychology), so also
should physiology proceed from the functional totality.
Thereby it would establish the etheric body as the fundamental concept of physiology.

More generally, we may say that man has an etheric
body in common with the plant, just as he has a physical
body in common with the minerals. Everything living has
its own etheric body—one that corresponds to the species
(in plants and animals) or to the ego (in man).[4] However,
"The human etheric body differs from that of plants and
animals through being organized to serve the purposes of
the thinking spirit."[5] Such statements keep us from imagining that all etheric bodies are somehow outwardly alike.

Man's etheric body (as well as his physical body) is raised
out of the realm of the "merely living" through the incor-
poration of the higher members of his being, the astral body
and the ego. Hence Rudolf Steiner's statement, which
sounds somewhat like a warning: "A human physical body
must never be subject merely to physical influences, a
human etheric body must never be subject merely to etheric
influences. They would disintegrate if they were."[6]

To obtain a true concept of the etheric body one must
grasp both its contour-dissolving aspect and its form-
maintaining aspect. Alternating between these two aspects,

the functions partake of the functional totality. Substances are called to life as soon as they enter the functional realm. They become different there, and consequently are different when they leave. The bark of the tree, for example, though it is leaving the etheric realm, is still on the way back to the physical; it has not yet arrived there.[7] Only when it decomposes in the soil has it fully arrived in the physical realm.

Thus it is possible to say that the etheric body becomes visible by virtue of the physical matter it takes up. The plant, said Rudolf Steiner, is an etheric form, filled out with physical substance. "Through the physical the etheric form becomes visible to us. What we actually see is the etheric form—the physical is only the means by which the etheric form becomes perceptible."[8]

The Etheric Body as a Time-Body

Just as the etheric body unifies the changing material substances in space, so also does it unify the different stages of form during development. It molds the forms that an individual passes through in its lifetime into a totality—a totality which cannot itself be perceived with the physical senses because it is the source out of which the sense-perceptible forms first arise. Strictly speaking, the joining of the forms is the task of the perceiver and concerns him only; nature, on the other hand, evolves the individual forms out of the totality, because for her the totality is primary. The temporal succession of forms is the result of an unfolding into the spatial dimension—a true "ex-plane-ation." For this reason Rudolf Steiner occasionally contrasted the etheric body as a time-body with the physical body as a spatial body.[9]

It was evidently such a relationship of the spatial and the temporal that Goethe had in mind when he spoke of his plant "type." The repeated expansion and contraction that he attributed to the "type" has a temporal character as well.

The human etheric body as a time-body is somewhat more difficult to comprehend than that of the plant. Instead of imagining a series of forms, one must rather think of the successive stages of human life with their accompanying psychological and spiritual conditions. That which in biology is a stage of form, is for the human being a phase of life filled with experiences. The real connection between the earlier and later phases of life is provided by the etheric body. Rudolf Steiner has given examples of how the experiences of childhood can become predispositions to disease or health.[10]

Rudolf Steiner has also described how the etheric body reveals itself as a body of time to a soul who has just crossed the threshold of death. For three days after death the soul experiences its whole past life spread out before it in a vast "panorama" or "tableau." The etheric body of man is then present as a continuous whole before him, just as earlier he had carried it as a continuous whole within him.[11]

The Etheric Body as the Bearer of Form and Heredity
(The Body of Formative Forces)

From the foregoing it is evident that the form of the living organism is mediated, if not determined, by the etheric body.

> One must imagine that in the plant, living substance is continually being separated out from the lifeless. In this living substance, the plant form appears as the result of the forces streaming in toward the earth. This results in a "stream of substance"; the lifeless is transformed into the living, the living is transformed into the lifeless. The organs of the plant arise within this stream.[12]

The life of the plant, therefore, "is brought to a formed condition within the etheric realm."[12] With the animal, however, the life within the etheric realm is kept in flow, and the form is introduced into the life through the astral organization. With the human being, also this astral process remains fluid. The sentient (astral) substance becomes transformed, and it is only in the ego-organization that "the inner and outer aspects of the human form arise."[12]

The specific form of the organism, which in plants arises within the etheric body and in animals and man arises in higher members, is transmitted through heredity to the offspring. Thus it is only in the plant that the form is passed on solely by the etheric body; in animals the inherited form is modified by the astral body; in man it is the ego-organization that determines the final form. (This form is derived from the "inherited model body" through the agency of the astral body and ego.[13]) That which was created by the lower members as a preliminary form, remains in the background as a kind of matrix for the formative activity, and can appear again in times of illness. Thus the bearer of heredity is significantly different in each of the three kingdoms; only in the plant is it the etheric body alone.

In these three kingdoms of nature there is one phenomenon that is particularly characteristic of the activity of the etheric body: the repetition of structural parts. In the plant kingdom this repetition is expressed in reproduction itself, and the leaf (the phyllome) is its living representative. In the animal kingdom, especially among the lower animals, there is a repetition of "homonomous" organs along the main axis. In Goethean terms, these repeated segments (metameres) provide a "sensory-supersensory" picture of the nature of the etheric body. According to Rudolf Steiner, the repetition of parts in a living being is due to the etheric body, which has the tendency to produce the same form again and again. Because of this tendency there also exists what we call "reproduction," the repetition of one's own kind. This is essentially due to the activity of the etheric body. Everything that is repetitive in living organisms can be traced back to the etheric principle. On the other hand, everything that brings the repetition to a conclusion, is a manifestation of the astral principle.[14]

When dealing with repetition, one need not think only of segmentation along an axis. There is also a two-dimensional repetition of organs on the exterior of the body or within it, for instance, the integumentary structures (hair, bristles, spines, scales, feathers, glands) or the internal structure of the sensory organs (the so-called receptors, the rods and cones in the retina of the eye, etc.). Ultimately, the repetition of tissue—muscles, bones, nerves—throughout the body, or even the cellular structure of the whole body, is also due to the etheric body. The proliferation of the cells, however can become antagonistic to the overall influence of the etheric body, as happens in tumor formation.[15]

In the formation of resting stages (resting spores and seeds, perennial buds, the statoblasts of the bryozoans, the eggs of animals), the physical activity of the etheric body disappears almost completely and the bodily substance becomes less complex (dedifferentiates). The suspended activity of the etheric body can enter in again later: the dampness of the earth and the sun's warmth awaken the plant seed, fertilization initiates the development of the animal ovum. The structural multiplication begins once again. When phenomena are juxtaposed in such a way, reproduction is revealed as a special case of the general "polymerizing" activity of the etheric body.

The form-creating power of the etheric body becomes most apparent in the regeneration of lost parts, whether this consists of the mere regrowth of a lost part, or the complete reorganization of an organism (so-called "regulation"). In an earlier work (*The Body of Formative Forces of the Living Being as an Object of Scientific Experience*[16]), the author first pointed to the interrelated significance of all the characteristic features of the etheric body:

1. The twofold or manifold occurrence of spatially separated daughter-forms, which maintain an inner relationship.
2. The development of juxtaposed daughter-forms which are mirror-images of one another (enantiomorphs).
3. The development of mirror-image reversals (inversions).
4. The meeting and merging of separate, inwardly related structures (e.g. the pathological development of a cyclopean eye).
5. The disappearance and reappearance of the total form and its parts (reproduction and heredity).

Since this work was published in 1924 it has become clear that several of these characteristic features could hardly have arisen without the participation of the astral body, and that in the third and fourth items above (e.g. the interchange of the unequal left and right claws of crabs and the pathological cyclopia of fishes) we were actually describing manifestations of the astral body. Nevertheless, these phenomena that are due primarily to the astral body, also reveal the mediating activity of the etheric body. Instead of the naive picture of "involuting through the fourth dimension," which I suggested at that time, we have today the possibility of a mathematical approach to the etheric (see below).

Avoiding Speculative Abstractions

The manner in which we have approached the concept of the etheric body has kept us from falling into the abstractions of *Naturphilosophie*, such as the "entelechy" of Driesch and others who are attempting to achieve a conceptual grasp of the autonomy of living things. As we wrote already in 1924 in the work cited, it is untenable simply to add a "vital factor" (even if conceived non-spatially) to the other factors that (one believes) constitute the living "system." A "factor" which makes a living whole out of the sum of the parts is itself no more than a part in disguise. Expressed differently, it is futile to try to comprehend a living organism with the supposedly "objective" notion of a "system" borrowed from physics. The specific laws of the living cannot be grasped in this way.[17] Such postulates, of which Mittasch[18] has enumerated more than a dozen, draw one away from definite and expressive manifestations of life and lead—explicitly or implicitly—to some version of teleology. It was Goethe, however, who broke with *Naturphilosophie* by declaring his "aversion to final causes."

The concept of the etheric body as we have introduced it is not abstraction but experience. It has no teleological implications, because it is derived from the supersensible perception of a field in which there exist formations and transformations, but no purposes.

The Etheric Body as Concept and Idea

The concept of the etheric body differs from all other "constructs," in that it is derived from supersensible *perception*. It originates in direct observation ("clairvoyance"), not from vague inferences. The etheric body is not a "factor," but a supersensible entity active in all living beings. Yet for normal consciousness the concept of the etheric body is to begin with like any other concept; it performs the necessary function of bringing order to the facts of sensory experience. Man is so constituted that in the act of perceiving he splits reality apart into percepts and concepts. He must reunite these in the act of knowing in order to recover full reality.[19] The full reality of the etheric body cannot be known until it is perceived as well as conceived, but the concept of the etheric body nevertheless makes the sense-perceptible phenomena of life intelligible.[20]

The concept of the etheric body, as Unger [21] has demonstrated so astutely, has yet another special significance. The etheric body lends itself particularly well to representation in conceptual form, for it has, so to speak, by its very nature a conceptual character. As long as one cannot, or chooses not to achieve direct supersensible perception oneself, the essence of the etheric body is best apprehended in conceptual form. At the same time, however, one must take into account that concepts as such are merely the shadows of higher spiritual realities; as they appear in ordinary consciousness, concepts are the end result of a process of "devitalization" ["*Herablähmung*"].[22]

The kinship of the etheric body and the living spiritual world—which has its shadows in our concepts—is shown particularly clearly where the etheric body is "freed" from its functions in the body. In this freed condition the etheric body forms the basis for man's free life of thought; this accounts for the remarkable correspondence between the formative processes of the body and the processes of thought.[23] The multiplication and differentiation of bodily structures corresponds to the repeatability and variability of thought structures; the development of physical right-left symmetry corresponds to the symmetrical structure of logic; the loss and regeneration of an organ corresponds to the forgetting and reconstructing of a train of thought, etc.[24]

There is a "dialectic of morphogenesis" just as there is a "morphology of thought-forms." These parallels exist because both morphogenesis and thinking have a common basis in the etheric body. Their fundamental connection is described by Rudolf Steiner:

The forces present in the etheric body become active as forces of growth and differentiation at the beginning of man's life on earth—most distinctly during the embryonic period. In the course of life some of these forces emancipate themselves from the formative activity and become the forces of thought. . . . It is of the greatest importance to know that the ordinary thought-forces of man are the refined forces of growth and differentiation.[25]

Wherever the astral body sets limits to growth (see p. 223) the etheric forces are set free from their original task and are able to become a kind of matrix for the formation of thoughts. The capabilities native to thinking (e.g. repetition, variation, logical opposition) reveal the formative activities which were previously working in the physical body. Rudolf Steiner has also described the particular manner in which the physical body participates in making thoughts and concepts conscious, but this aspect lies beyond our present scope. Likewise, the enormous significance which all this has for education must be passed over here.[26]

For the more elementary understanding of the etheric body sought here, this dual nature is of great significance: a portion of its forces remains "true to its task at birth," the other portion manifests as thought.[27] The continuity of the two portions appears never to be lost entirely; whenever thinking slackens its activity it reverts to making connections based on bodily or instinctive influences. This can occur with fatigue or illness. It can lead even to symbolic hallucinations of the content of thought (Silberer's phenomenon) and to images of bodily organs that are hardly distinguishable from dreams.[28]

On the other hand, the etheric body is experienced in a more immediate and undistorted way in "pure thinking" (also termed "sense-free thinking" by Rudolf Steiner because it does not depend on sensory observation).[29] He says, "We learn to recognize how one thought interweaves with another within the mind, how one thought seeks another, even when the connections are not suggested by sensory observation. What is essential is that we discover that the thought world has an inner life of its own; when we are truly thinking we are already within a living, supersensible world. We say to ourselves: There is something within us which constitutes an organism of thinking, and indeed we are one with it."[29] From the context of the quote it is clear that this "something" refers to the part of the etheric body which liberates itself from organic activity in early childhood (at the time of the second dentition).[30]

Thus, those unwilling or unable to enter into supersensible perception may nevertheless recognize in the experience of the world of concepts a valid approach to the nature of the etheric body.

The Inadequacy of the "Field" Concept

Through having approached the nature of the etheric body from two sides—the morphological and the mental—the inadequacy of the concept of "biological fields" quickly becomes evident. This concept, analogous to the field concept in physics, is supposed to explain how the material particles of living substance are synthesized into an organized whole. The "building plan" is usually regarded as an "immaterial factor" existing over and above the "building blocks," similar to the relationship obtaining between a magnetic field and iron filings.

For the interpretation of physical facts, the introduction of the field concept was without a doubt a step forward. But for understanding the manifestations of life it is more like a hindering half-truth. The attempt to deduce the rich diversity of biological phenomena from a field of force (no matter how detailed), inevitably diverts our attention from the phenomena and does not further our insight into them. As has already been indicated, it is not a matter here of merely adding to the physical a new stratum of forces conceived in analogy to the physical forces. By virtue of its etheric body, an organism conforms to laws that are quite distinct from the laws of the physical world. Rudolf Steiner gave an important key to the conceptual understanding of the difference between the laws of the physical world and the etheric. We will attempt to describe this in the following two sections.

The Peripheral Forces versus the Central Forces

Rudolf Steiner first formulated the polarity of the peripheral and the central forces in mathematical language in 1921.[31] Here we would like to quote a later formulation (to our knowledge, the last before his death) because it presupposes no mathematical background.

> One will be able to say of those phenomena which take their course in the lifeless realm: they reveal themselves as subject to forces which radiate out from the essence of matter, from the (relative) center-point to the periphery. In the phenomena of life, however, the material substances are ruled by forces working from without inward, toward the (relative) center-point. When it becomes part of a living organism, matter must withdraw from the forces streaming outward and give itself over to the forces streaming inward. It is then drawn into the forces which stream in from the cosmos on all sides toward the earth. . . . From all sides these forces are active, as if they were striving toward the center of the earth.[32]

This is to be understood as a kind if impressionistic description of the etheric body. The totality of forces streaming toward the earth from cosmic space is a picture of what the trained spiritual researcher perceives, a spiritual Imagination. For the everyday thinking consciousness, it is described here pictorially. The etheric forces are active, says Rudolf Steiner, "as if they were striving toward the center of the earth." This manner of expressing things is advantageous if we are seeking to grasp and visualize the polarity of earth and cosmos, or non-living and living. An earlier passage from the same work reads: "The physical laws work as if streaming outward from the earth, the etheric laws as if streaming in toward the earth from all sides."[33] This metaphorical description brings one very close to the impression that clairvoyant consciousness receives. The clear contrast of the two modes of activity, however, should be regarded as an exercise for our conceptual imagination.

The implication of the foregoing is that the etheric body should not be imagined as existing in ordinary space at all. For if one says, as Rudolf Steiner does, that the etheric forces do not proceed from points in space, but rather from the infinite periphery, one has posited a kind of space that is the opposite of the usual one. Such a "counterspace" is conceivable, and indeed its mathematical characteristics have been derived. Just how wonderfully "negative" space corresponds to and includes the characteristics of the etheric realm has been demonstrated mathematically by Adams and Locher,[34] following the indications of Rudolf Steiner.

To understand the nature of the etheric body, it is absolutely necessary to place it in such a counterspace. Conceptualizations that for reasons of naiveté or ease avoid this, must end sooner or later in contradiction or absurdity. The "forces streaming from the periphery toward the earth" have no spatial starting-points, and unlike with other forces, distance cannot weaken them. They do not converge from different directions onto particular points having spatially predetermined coordinates. The reason why particular substances are grasped by the formative forces and others are not, does not have to do with the spatial configuration, but rather with the inner affinity between the formative etheric realm and the matter which is becoming formed. Even in its physical state, the physical matter of the organism must be in a condition in which the workings of the etheric can take hold of it. This happens, not because of its position in space, but because of an inner affinity. In the earth's present condition, the material preservers of the continuity of life are always minute, hardened structures such as spores, seeds, eggs, "eyes," etc. Moistening and fertilization, as we discussed earlier (p. 223), prepare the germ for the intervention of etheric forces.

The totality which approaches the earth from all sides is itself a potential form; biologically speaking, it is a specific form—the form of a species—that is on its way to renewed manifestation. In man, however, this renewing impulse does not approach him from the present cosmic environment, but rather from a past environment, via his embryonic life.[35]

The Etheric Body in "Configured" Counterspace

In contrast to the more or less inert and homogeneous space with which we are familiar, the etheric formative forces exist in a space that is differentiated and "configured." Thus, the nature of the substances which "come to rest" within this space is dependent upon their location. The common notion that every particle of a substance is alike is overthrown. A substance is what it is, only within the context of the space it occupies at any moment. It is possible, therefore, that different, even contradictory processes occur within the apparently tiny space of a single cell. In 1937 Bertalanffy wrote, "Let us observe for example a liver cell: it turns glycogen into sugar, and vice versa, produces urea and uric acid from amino acids and ammonia, breaks down hemoglobin, produces bile acids and has the ability to retain or render harmless the toxins which are brought to it. In a cell whose size is about one-hundredth that of the head of a pin, at least ten, and probably many more chemical processes are occurring simultaneously."[36] That the cell can exist at all in this medley, is due to the fact that it is maintained not from within but from the periphery. Rudolf Steiner expressed this by saying that in a single cell the entire cosmos is active.[37]

This compressing of many contradictory processes into a tiny space can only be comprehended if one realizes that the contents of the cell exist in a "counterspace" that is just as infinite as the ordinary space which surrounds the cell.

The above-mentioned investigations by Adams and Locher allow the relationship of the organs within one and the same organism to be considered in their full diversity and differentiation. Thereby it is seen that organs may be closely related even though they are not adjacent anatomically; they are, as it were, adjacent within counterspace. Examples of such "etheric neighbors" are the kidneys and the organs of sight, or the large intestine and the forebrain. In the field of pathology, many instances are known of the same disease taking hold of organs which are situated far apart, while the intervening regions of the body remain unaffected.

The Human Etheric Body

In order to comprehend the etheric body completely, one must consider, as was stressed at the beginning, that in man its modifying and differentiating forces belong ultimately to the astral body and the ego; the etheric body thus

functions in man on a level two developmental stages higher
than in the plant. Rudolf Steiner describes this vividly:

> From all sides these etheric forces stream, as if striving
> toward the center of the earth. They would be compelled
> to tear the earthly matter to pieces, to dissolve it into
> complete formlessness, did there not enter into this
> "space of forces" the modifying influences of the extra-
> terrestrial heavenly bodies. . . .
>
> . . . Throughout its life the plant takes up into it-
> self the etheric forces which stream onto the earth. In
> an individualized condition, man carries these forces
> from the time of embryonic development onward. Dur-
> ing his life, he takes *out of himself* what the plant
> receives continually from the universe. . . . A force
> which is actually cosmic in origin—destined originally
> to stream in toward the earth—operates in man out-
> ward from particular organs like the liver or the lung.
> It has undergone a metamorphosis of direction.[38]

Thus the human etheric body has quite diverse regions.
In some regions it is subject to the physical body, in others it
is active in relative purity, and in still others the activity of
the astral body or the ego predominates. In all of these
regions, the occurrence of specific substances can be understood as the manifestation of the changing interaction of the
four members of the human being.[39]

The Collaborative Activities of the Etheric Body
The etheric body of the plant works in from the extra-
terrestrial to summon the substances to life and, in conjunction with the "sidereal" (astral) influences, to give the plant
its form. The human etheric body is in a somewhat comparable state only in sleep; but even there, the activity of the
astral body and the ego within the organism during the wak-

ing state are present as subtle after-effects. When these after-effects wear off, the astral body and the ego return, and the human being wakes up again. These changing relations among the four members of the human being constitute a metamorphosis of the direct correspondence between the formative activity of the body and the thinking activity of the soul (described p. 226ff.). In conclusion, we may mention some further metamorphoses in which the etheric body is critical:

1. In the act of forming mental pictures, voluntary as well as involuntary, the etheric body loosens itself slightly from its physical attachment.
2. In imaginative activity (fantasy) man's thinking organization adapts itself to the rhythm of the circulation of the blood—an inner breathing takes place.[40]
3. When something is remembered, the experience becomes "imprinted" in the organism at the "boundary" of the physical and the etheric bodies. In the act of recollection, these imprints are deciphered again by the soul.[41]
4. In the emergence of dreams just prior to waking, the sleep experiences of the astral body and the ego are reflected, more or less confusedly, in the etheric body and in its formative forces.[42]
5. When the astral body and ego are partially immersed in the etheric and physical bodies (not reaching as far as the external senses), feelings and emotions arise in the soul.[43]

One could not ascribe responsibility for any of the activities listed above to the etheric body alone, yet it is essential in each one. Our view is thereby directed toward capabilities which the etheric body carries within itself, but which only become manifest in its collaboration with the other members of the human being.

There are indeed further dimensions to the etheric body, such as its participation in the activity of supersensible perception, but it is not possible to explore these here. Similarly, it is also not possible for us to describe the origin of the etheric body either in cosmic evolution or in the development of the individual, even though its nature and function would be greatly elucidated thereby.[44]

Notes

References to untranslated works of Rudolf Steiner are given by GA number (GA = Gesamtausgabe = Collected Edition, published by Rudolf Steiner Verlag, Dornach, Switzerland).

1. This contribution has been taken essentially unchanged from the "Anthroposophisch-medizinisches Jahrbuch," volume 3, Stuttgart 1952.

2. We owe this to a verbal communication by the late Dr. Otto Palmer.

3. *Translator's Note*: For the development of higher perception and consciousness see Steiner, Rudolf. *Knowledge of the Higher Worlds and Its Attainment* (1904). Spring Valley, N.Y.: Anthroposophic Press 1947; *The Case for Anthroposophy* (1917). London: Rudolf Steiner Press 1970, esp. chapter 1; and *Esoteric Development: Selected Lectures and Writings from the Works of Rudolf Steiner*. Spring Valley, N.Y.: Anthroposophic Press 1982, esp. chapter 2.

4. Steiner, R. *An Outline of Occult Science* (1910). Spring Valley, N.Y.: Anthroposophic Press 1972. Chapter 2.

5. Steiner, R. *Theosophy* (1904). Spring Valley, N.Y.: Anthroposophic Press 1971. Chapter 1, section 4.

6. Steiner, R. and Ita Wegman, *Fundamentals of Therapy* (1925). 4th ed. London: Rudolf Steiner Press 1983. Chapter 1.

7. See note 6. Chapter 5.

8. Steiner, R. *The Mystery of the Trinity*. London and New York: Rudolf Steiner Pub. Co. 1947. Lecture of July 28, 1922.

9. Steiner, R. *Anthroposophical Leading Thoughts* (1924/25). London: Rudolf Steiner Press 1973. Number 29.

10. Steiner, R. *The Essentials of Education*. London: Rudolf Steiner Press 1982. Lecture of April 8, 1924.

11. See note 4. Chapter 3, p. 61f.

12. See note 6. Chapter 5.

13. Steiner, R. *Curative Education*. London: Rudolf Steiner Press 1972. Lecture of June 25, 1924.

14. See Steiner, R. *Geisteswissenschaftliche Menschenkunde*. GA 107, 4th ed. 1979. Lecture of November 2, 1908,

15. Steiner, R. *Spiritual Science and Medicine*. London: Rudolf Steiner Press 1948. Lecture of March 27, 1920.

16. Poppelbaum, H. *Der Bildekräfteleib der Lebewesen als Gegenstand wissenschaftlicher Erfahrung*. Stuttgart: Kommende Tag Verlag 1924. (Not yet in translation.)

17. This is cogently demonstrated by T. von Uexküll and E. Grassi in their book *Von Ursprung und Grenzen der Geisteswissenschaften und Naturwissenschaften*. Bern: 1950.

18. Mittasch, A. *Entelechie*. Basel: 1952.

19. Steiner, R. *The Philosophy of Freedom* (1894). Spring Valley, N.Y.: Anthroposophic Press 1964. Esp. chapters 4 & 5. For Steiner's basic epistemology, see also *Truth and Knowledge* (1892). Blauvelt, N.Y.: Steinerbooks Publications 1963; and *A Theory of Knowledge Implicit in Goethe's World Conception* (1886). Spring Valley, N.Y.: Anthroposophic Press 1968.

20. *Translator's Note*: As a living totality, the etheric body is *perceptible*, but only to specially trained, supersensible perception (see note 3). The content of this perception, like any perceptual experience, is *intelligible* only with the appropriate concept, which is accessible also to the non-clairvoyant. The concept of the etheric body can therefore be used to *understand* the phenomena of life, even if these cannot yet be perceived as a totality.

The concept of the etheric body forms a link between ordinary consciousness and higher (supersensible) consciousness. In the text this concept is derived from supersensible perception, but it can also be derived logically. Most investigators, however, are not confident enough in their own thinking to discover that an etheric world (and indeed a whole spiritual realm) *must* exist in addition to the world they can perceive: They cannot get beyond "vague inferences." In his philosophical works (see note 19), Rudolf Steiner placed great emphasis on the development of a mode of thinking that could be independent of the perceived world; with this mode of "pure thinking" it is indeed possible to deduce logically the concept of the etheric body (cf. Unger, Carl. *Principles of Spiritual Science*. Spring Valley, N.Y.: Anthroposophic Press 1976, p. 50ff.).

21. Unger, C. *Language of the Conscious Soul* (1930). Spring Valley N.Y.: St. George Books 1983. Chapter 5.

22. Steiner, R. *The Case for Anthroposophy* (1917). London: Rudolf Steiner Press 1970. Chapter 4.

23. Compare the essay by C. Lindenau in this volume (p. 199ff.). See also note 9. Number 100.

24. See note 15. Lecture of March 23, 1920.

25. See note 6. Chapter 3.

26. See Steiner, R. *The Education of the Child in the Light of Anthroposophy* (1907). 2nd ed. London: Rudolf Steiner Press 1965.

27. See note 6. Chapter 1.

28. See also the last section of the present essay.

29. See note 4. Chapter 5, p. 294ff.

30. See note 26. Page 20ff.

31. Steiner, R. *Das Verhältnis der verschiedenen naturwissenschaftlichen Gebiete zur Astronomie*. GA 323, 2nd ed. 1983. Lecture of January 10, 1921.

32. See note 6. Chapter 3.

33. See note 6. Chapter 1.

34. Adams, George. *Physical and Ethereal Spaces* (1933). London: Rudolf Steiner Press 1965.
— *Strahlende Weltgestaltung* (1934). 2nd ed. Dornach: Philosophisch-Anthroposophischer Verlag 1965.
— and Olive Whicher. *The Plant between Sun and Earth* (1952). London: Rudolf Steiner Press 1980.

Locher-Ernst, Louis. *Projektive Geometrie* (1940). 2nd ed. Dornach: Philosophisch-Anthroposophischer Verlag 1980.

35. See Poppelbaum, H. *Schicksalsrätsel: Verkörperung und Wiederverkörperung* (1949). 3rd ed. Dornach: Philosophisch-Anthroposophischer Verlag 1980.

36. Bertalanffy, L. v. *Das Gefüge des Lebens*. Leipzig and Berlin: Teubner 1937. Page 80.

37. See note 31. Lecture of January 1, 1921.

38. See note 6. Chapter 3.

39. See Steiner, R. *The World of the Senses and the World of the Spirit*. N. Vancouver: Steiner Book Centre 1947. Lectures of December 29 & 30, 1912.

40. See note 9. Letter of March 22, 1925.

41. See note 22. Chapter 1. Also see Poppelbaum, H. "Welche Rolle spielen physischer und ätherischer Leib beim Erinnern?" in *Menschengemässe Natur-erkenntnis* (collected essays). Basel: 1942.

42. See Steiner, R. *The Evolution of Consciousness.* London: Rudolf Steiner Press 1979. Lecture of August 24, 1923.

43. See Steiner, R. *Cosmosophy*, vol. 1. Spring Valley, N.Y.: Anthroposophic Press 1985. Lecture of September 30, 1921.

44. See note 35.

About the Authors

Jochen Bockemühl

Born 1928 in Dresden. Studied zoology, botany, chemistry and geology in Dresden and Tubingen. Received doctorate in 1955 for work on the faunal ecology of soil-dwelling insects. At the same time familiarized himself with the epistemology of Rudolf Steiner and the ideas of anthroposophy. Since 1956 has worked in the Research Laboratory at the Goetheanum in Dornach. Since 1971 Director of the Natural Science Section at the Goetheanum.

Anthroposophical publications in the semi-annual journal "Elemente der Naturwissenschaft" (edited by Bockemühl and Georg Maier). Books: *In Partnership with Nature.* Wyoming, R.I. 1981; *Sterbende Wälder—eine Bewusstseinsfrage.* Dornach 1984.

Christof Lindenau

Born 1928 in Danzig. Studied philosophy and literature in Freiburg (Breisgau). Presently full-time Administrator for the Anthroposophical Society at Nordrhein-Westfalen, Germany.

Anthroposophical publications: *Der übende Mensch.* Stuttgart 1976; and *Soziale Dreigliederung.* Stuttgart 1983.

Georg Maier

Born 1933 in Stuttgart. Attended Waldorf school in England from 1939–1946. Beginning 1952 studied in Stuttgart and Munich. Doctoral thesis (1960) on the theme "Excitation Spectra of Mixed Crystals." 1961–1969 researcher in solid-state physics at the Institute for Reactor Research in Würenlingen and at the Nuclear Research Facility in Jülich. Since 1969 has worked in the Research Laboratory at the Goetheanum.

Present research interests: optics of image transformations, with publications in "Elemente der Naturwissenschaft."

Ernst-August Müller

Born 1925 in Uengsterrode/Meissner. Studied physics and mathematics at the University of Göttingen. Received doctorate in 1953 for work on supersonic streaming phenomena. Began teaching 1961. Full professor of applied mechanics and the physics of streaming at the University of Göttingen 1969. Research area: gas dynamics, turbulence, streaming acoustics.

Publications in the field of an anthroposophically oriented physics of streaming in the journal "Elemente der Naturwissenschaft."

Hermann Poppelbaum

Born 1891 in Frankfurt a.M. studied zoology and botany in Freiburg i.Br. and Munich. Received doctorate in 1913 for work on gynandromorphic butterfly hybrids. Began working in 1921 in the Anthroposophical Society in Germany. From 1939 to 1948 active as teacher and lecturer in the United States. 1949 member of Executive Council of General Anthroposophical Society. Director of the Pedagogical Section and later the Natural Science Section at the Goetheanum.

Primary scientific publications: *Man and Animal* (1928); *A New Zoology* (1936); *Menschengemässe Naturerkenntnis*, collected essays (1942); *New Light on Heredity and Evolution* (1961).

Dietrich Rapp

Born 1941 in Tübingen. Studied physics and philosophy in Tübingen, Hamburg and Göttingen. Since 1965, under the auspices of the Max Planck Institute for Streaming Research, has studied gas dynamics and streaming instability in connection with the investigation of etheric activity.

Publications on philosophical and scientific themes have appeared in the monthly journal "Die Drei."

Wolfgang Schad

Born 1935 in Biberach/Riss. Studied biology, chemistry and physics in Marburg and Munich and pedagogy at the Pedagogical College of Göttingen (until 1961). Taught in public high school and since 1962 at the Waldorf school in Pforzheim and, since 1975, in Stuttgart. Also active in Stuttgart in the Waldorf Teachers Seminar, in the research division of the Federation of Waldorf Schools, and in the Private Technical School for Social Pedagogy.

Publications: numerous articles in the journals "Elemente der Naturwissenschaft," "Die Drei" and "Erziehungskunst" with scientific, medical and art historical themes. Books: *Man and Mammals* (1971); with Ekkehard Schweppenhäuser, *Blütenspaziergänge: Uebungen im Naturbetrachten* (1975).

Arthur G. Zajonc

Born 1949 in Boston. Doctorate in physics from the University of Michigan (1976). Postdoctoral fellow at the Joint Institute for Laboratory Astrophysics at the University of Colorado and the National Bureau of Standards in Boulder (1976–78). Visiting professor at the Ecole Normale Supérieure in Paris (1981–82) and at the Max Planck Institute for Quantum Optics in Garching (1984). Currently associate professor of physics at Amherst College.

Publications on collision physics, lasers, quantum mechanics, history and philosophy of science, and Goethe's color theory, in various journals. Co-editor with F. Amrine of forthcoming volume of essays on Goethean science entitled *The Eye's Mind*.

Translation Credits

Introduction — John Davy

Elements and Ethers: Modes of Observing the World —
  John Davy

Light and the Pictorial Appearance of the World —
  John Meeks

Streaming: A Picture of the Etheric — John Davy

The Formative Movements of Plants — John Davy

Scientific Thinking as an Approach to the Etheric —
  Frederick Amrine

*Life Organization and Thought Organization: Concerning the
  Dual Nature of the Human Etheric Body* — Alan P. Cottrell

The Concept and Action of the Etheric Body —
  Malcolm Gardner

The English translations were edited by John Davy and
Malcolm Gardner